Mechanical Engineering Design 1
Organisation and Control

Mechanical Engineering Design 1 Organisation and Control

M. A. Parker, MEd, IEng.(CEI), MIMGTech.E

Technical Education Officer, British Standards Institution.
Formerly Senior Lecturer at Hong Kong Polytechnic in Engineering Drawing and Design.

L. J. Dennis, BSc(Eng), Dip. NEC

Formerly Principal Lecturer in Engineering Design in the Faculty of Engineering, Science and Mathematics, Middlesex Polytechnic.

Hutchinson
London Sydney Auckland Johannesburg

Hutchinson Education

An imprint of Century Hutchinson Ltd
62-65 Chandos Place, London WC2N 4NW

Century Hutchinson Australia (Pty) Ltd
89-91 Albion Street, Surry Hills,
New South Wales 2010, Australia

Century Hutchinson New Zealand Ltd
PO Box 40-086, Glenfield, Auckland 10, New Zealand

Century Hutchinson South Africa (Pty) Ltd
PO Box 337, Bergvlei 2012, South Africa

First published 1989

Printed and bound in Great Britain by
Anchor Press Ltd, Tiptree, Essex

ISBN 0 09 175676 6

Contents

Preface vii

1 **Design drawing practice** 1

2 **Control of drawing and design work** 11

3 **Dimensioning and tolerancing** 25

4 **Surface texture** 71

5 **Computer aided design** 82

6 **Costs** 91

7 **Design exercises** 105

Appendix 133

Preface

The two previous books in this series, Engineering Drawing with Worked Examples, Volumes 1 and 2, have, over the years since they were first published, proved very popular with students of engineering drawing at all levels, and with young draughtpersons aspiring to improve their ability.

The advent of the 'Finniston' approach to the teaching of engineering and the welcome insistence by course validating authorities on practical design work in engineering courses, have encouraged the authors to write these two further volumes. They aim to extend the material of the previous volumes into areas of mechanical engineering design which a designer needs to understand, and to provide insights into the methodical investigation and application of thought based on current practice which are necessary to produce successful engineering designs.

Engineering design is a vast area of study. So, whereas the previous volumes were definitive, these are not exhaustive and all-embracing treatises but a series of introductions to further study. Therefore, the reader is encouraged to consult textbooks, magazines, manufacturers' catalogues and data sheets and other reference material in order to extend his knowledge of the topics introduced in each chapter.

Among such reference material, particular attention is drawn to British Standards, and the authors are grateful for permission from the British Standards Institution to reprint extracts from some of their publications.

The authors would like to acknowledge much help from teaching colleagues and from members of committees connected with examining and teaching at undergraduate level. No specific reference has been made to them or to the many sources of opinion, fact and theory contained in the pages which follow, which have been arranged as far as possible to form a coherent whole. The authors' debt to such sources is not thereby lessened and they hope that, in pointing out and adding to the material that is provided here for tiro designers, all may find enjoyment.

London 1988

M. A. P.
L. J. D.

1 Design drawing practice

An engineering drawing is not a pictorial representation of an object. Instead, by using accepted conventions, most of which are understood world-wide, it conveys specific and complete information about the size, shape, dimensions, finish, and so on, of the object to an informed reader.

The student will already be familiar with many of these conventions, such as the two types of orthographic projection with their international symbols and the use of sections and sectional views to depict the internal features of an object. Full coverage of the basic principles and conventions of engineering drawing is provided by the three parts of BS 308 Engineering drawing practice. PP 7308 Engineering drawing practice for schools and colleges, also published by the British Standards Institution, covers the main areas of the first two parts of BS 308 in an abbreviated form.

Thinking in scale

The student should already be used to planning the positions of the views of a drawing on the paper, but it is also important to choose the best size of presentation, that is, the scale of the drawing. Thus, a large object will need to be drawn smaller than full size and a small item larger than full size. Drawings of small items to an enlarged scale sometimes contain an actual size view to avoid any confusion over how large the part really is (see Figure 1.1). However, prints or reproductions of drawings are not always made at the same size as the originals so the actual size view may not, in fact, be actual size.

Sometimes, for clarity of presentation or for dimensioning, it is necessary to enlarge only a part of the item being drawn. Figure 1.2 shows this practice applied to a thread undercut.

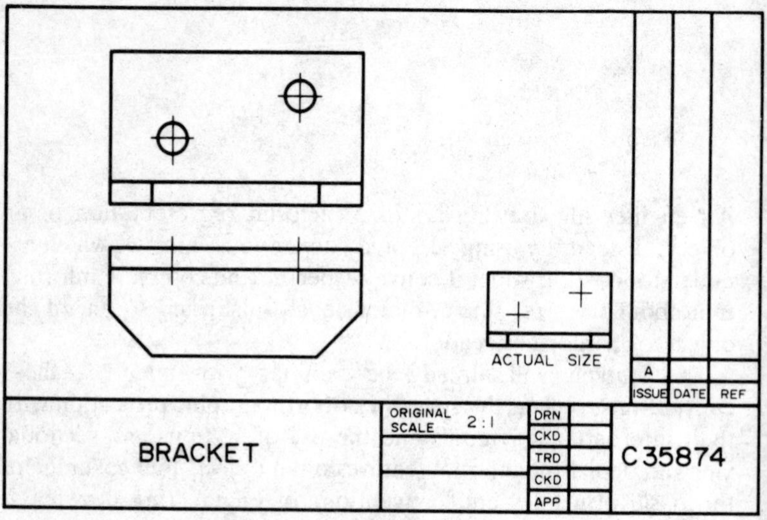

Fig. 1.1 *Use of Actual Size View*

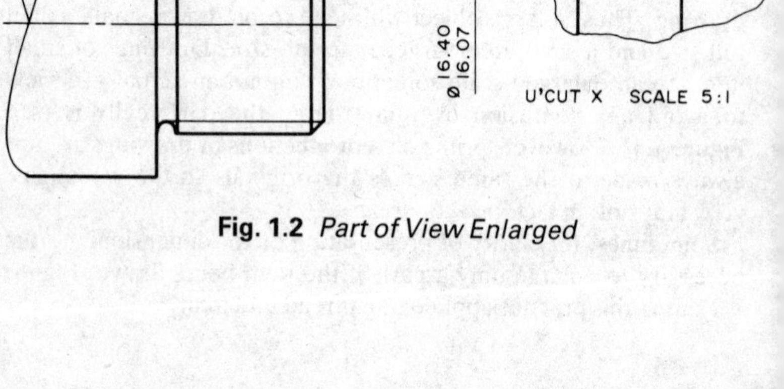

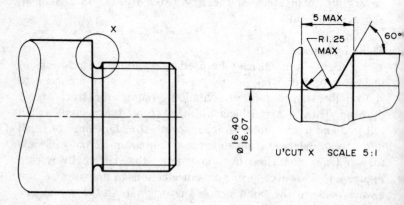

Fig. 1.2 *Part of View Enlarged*

BS 308 recommends the following scales and method of inscribing them on drawings.

Full size: 1:1

On drawings smaller than full size:

1:2	1:20	1:200
1:5	1:50	1:500
1:10	1:100	1:1000

On drawings larger than full size:

2:1	20:1	200:1
5:1	50:1	500:1
10:1	100:1	1000:1

Choosing views

Engineers might not be expected to think of their drawings as works of art, but nevertheless, a good, well-arranged drawing makes an immediate impact, to which correctly chosen views contribute. No more views should be drawn than are sufficient to describe the part completely, and in some cases this means only one view, or one view and a note. For example, simple cylindrical parts, of which Figure 1.3 is an example, may need only one view.

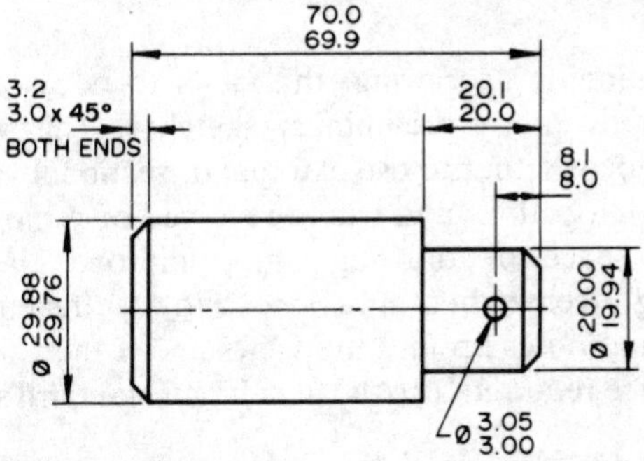

Fig. 1.3 *Cylindrical Part Completely Described in One View*

More complicated cylindrical parts can be drawn adequately using only a half sectional view with suitable dimensioning, as shown in Figure 1.4. Parts made from flat sheet can be described fully by one view and a note giving the material thickness (see Figure 1.5).

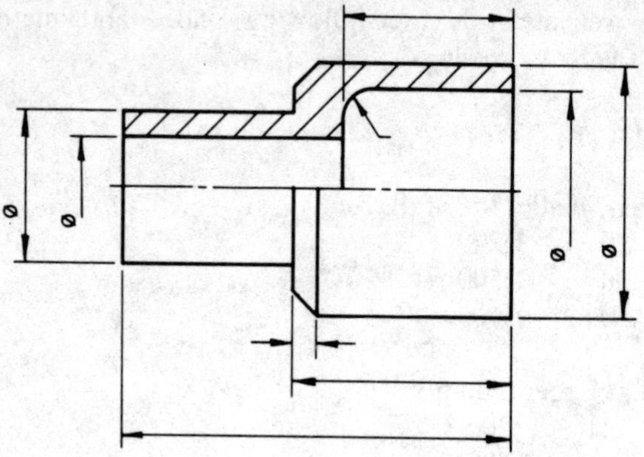

Fig. 1.4 *Use of Half Sectional View*

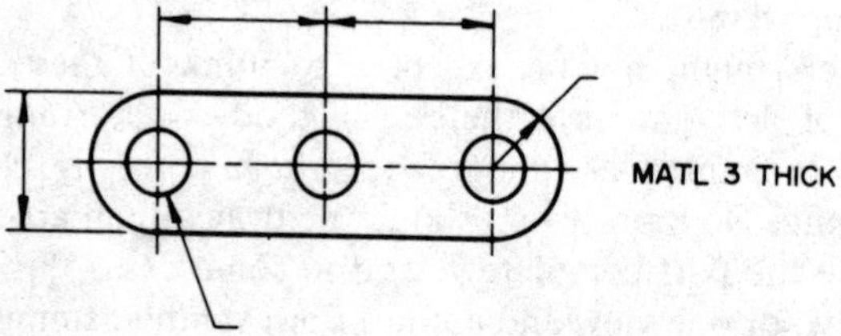

Fig. 1.5 *View Replaced by a Note*

Before beginning a drawing, the views to be used should be chosen mentally or by preliminary sketches. This will make it easier to decide whether to use external or sectional views, partial views or partial sections and where revolved or removed sections would save space or drawing time, improve clarity or aid dimensioning. Remember always to allow sufficient space for dimensions and notes around the views and if there is any doubt about the space required, use the next larger standard sheet size.

Speed drawing

Planning the drawing mentally before beginning will save time wasted on indecision later. Time will also be saved by following good practices as the drawing proceeds. Work on all the views together rather than completing them one at a time. Lay out first the main centre lines and outlines of the views before adding smaller features, and follow these with dimensions and notes.

Draw as many circles and radii as possible with one setting of the compasses or bows, or use a radius aid or circle template. Use the setting of compasses or bows from the centre lines of diameters to set off rectangular views of cylinders. Draw lines in two views at once with one setting of the straight edge wherever possible and when lining-in the drawing, draw all horizontal lines together working from the top to the bottom and all vertical lines together working from the left to the right. These points are illustrated in Figure 1.6. In an observed exercise, one hour in three was saved on a relatively simple drawing by careful preparatory thinking and good working practices.

Remember that a repeated criticism of young draughtspersons by employers is that they do not understand the necessity for speed in draughting to keep drawing office costs down, and that these costs have to be borne by the finished product.

Types of drawings

Designs usually begin as a *scheme*, which the designer prepares to formulate his solution to the design brief. A scheme shows the complete assembly of the design or a major sub-assembly of it and is usually undimensioned except for critical maximum or minimum requirements, fits denoted by their basic sizes with letter and number designations from BS 4500 ISO limits and fits, and the dimensions and requirements of such items as springs. The materials of the parts and any heat treatment or finish will also be specified by the designer. Design offices often combine prints of scheme drawings to the same scale by different designers to produce an overall picture of a large assembly such as an engine. Such drawings are sometimes called *long-toms* after their originator.

Detail drawings are often produced in a different office (the detail drawing office) from that responsible for schemes, or, in a small company, by junior members of the design team. Detail draughtsmen work from the scheme, scaling and working out undimensioned features, to produce a drawing for each part (a 'detail'). These detail drawings give all the information necessary for the part to be made to fulfil its function.

Assembly drawings are prepared using the dimensions from the finished detail drawings and this provides a secondary check of their accuracy. Each detail is identified on the assembly drawing

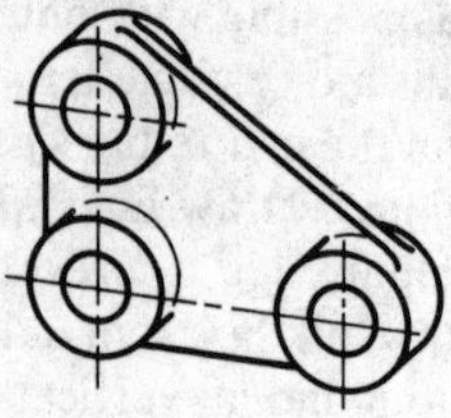

Pictorial view of component

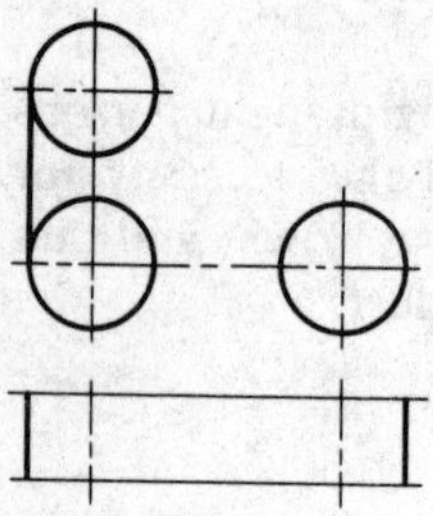

Stage I
Lay out centre lines. Draw bosses in upper view. Draw boss thickness in lower view allowing space between views for dimensions. Draw extreme vertical lines in both views in finished thickness.

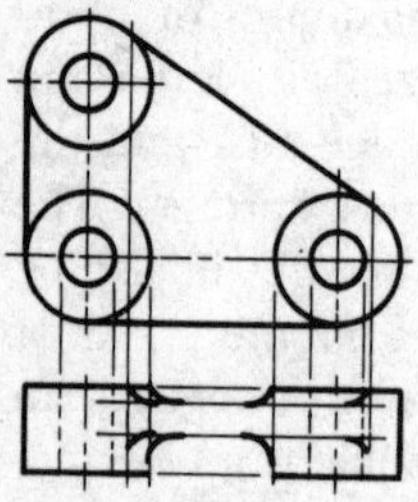

Stage 2
Draw holes in upper view and project to lower view as hidden lines. Complete web in upper view. Draw web thickness in lower view and project fillet radii runouts from upper view. Line in bosses in lower view and add fillet radii.

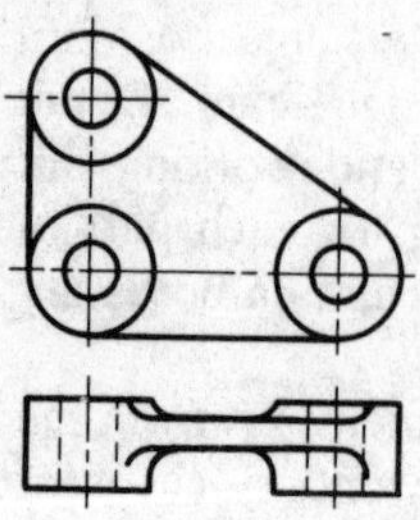

Stage 3
Line in web in lower view. Complete drawing by erasing construction lines and adding dimensions.

Fig. 1.6 *Speed Drawing*

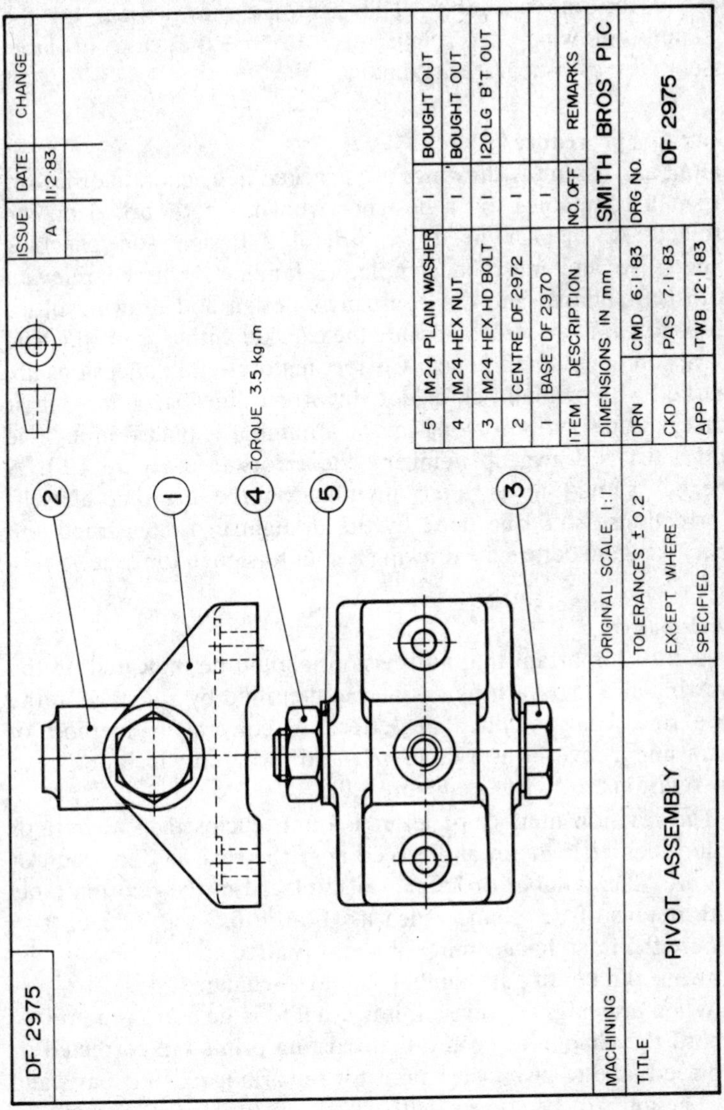

Fig. 1.7 *Assembly Drawing Including Item List*

and cross-referenced to a *parts or item list*. This list gives the names of the parts, the drawing numbers and how many are needed for one assembly. The item list may appear on the assembly drawing, see Figure 1.7 or, in the case of large assemblies, as a separate document.

Checking procedure

Detail and assembly drawings are checked in a separate office or, in small companies, by a designer who has not worked on the project. A checker needs considerable design and checking experience and must be completely familiar with the relevant British Standards and the company's design and drawing office procedures. It is usual to provide the checker with a print which he marks up in coloured pencil. Correct features and dimensions are marked with a small tick or dot. Incorrect dimensions have their correct values written alongside or a number is placed in a circle and a list is drawn up itemizing the errors (see Figure 1.8). A checker should never alter anything on the drawing himself. Corrections should be done by the draughtsman concerned and checked again before the drawing is countersigned for issue.

Revisions

It is most important that all revisions should be indicated on the drawing and that each new issue be identified by a change in the date and issue number or letter. A convenient method of recording a revision is a table on the drawing in which details of the revision are given (see Figure 1.9).

The revision number or letter is often enclosed in a circle or other geometric figure and placed near the revised dimension or feature. The number or letter is also placed in the revision table with details of the change such as '12.5 ± 0.2 was 12.5 ± 0.4'. Where the interchangeability of a part is affected by a revision the drawing number or part number should be changed.

When drawings are revised, it is usual to issue a form or note to record the change to ensure that existing prints are corrected or replaced, and to give instructions for reworking existing parts and the action to be taken with work in progress. Sometimes modifications permit a Mark I version, which has already been sold, to be uprated to a Mark II and the attention of other departments must be drawn to this by a suitable system.

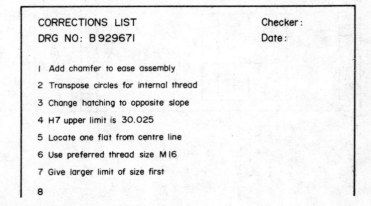

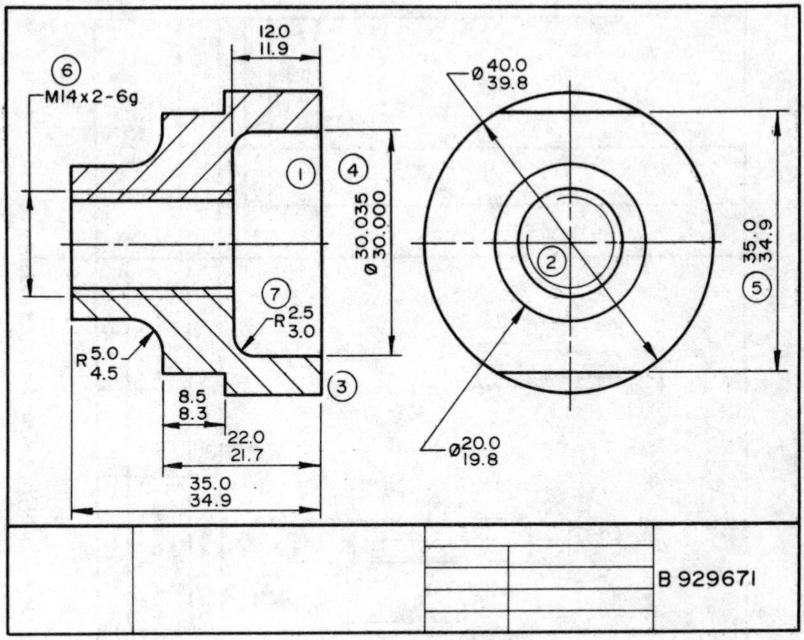

CORRECTIONS LIST
DRG NO: B 929671

Checker:
Date:

1 Add chamfer to ease assembly

2 Transpose circles for internal thread

3 Change hatching to opposite slope

4 H7 upper limit is 30.025

5 Locate one flat from centre line

6 Use preferred thread size M16

7 Give larger limit of size first

8

Fig. 1.8 *Checked Drawing and Corrections List*

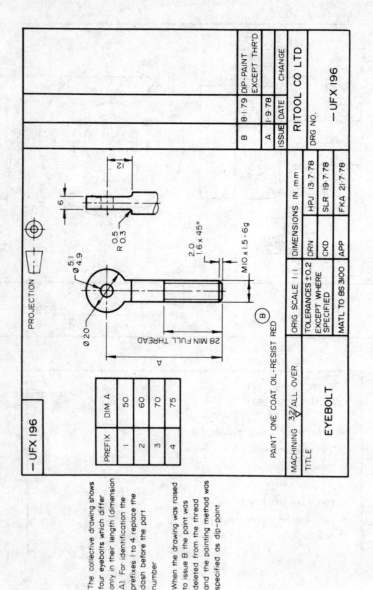

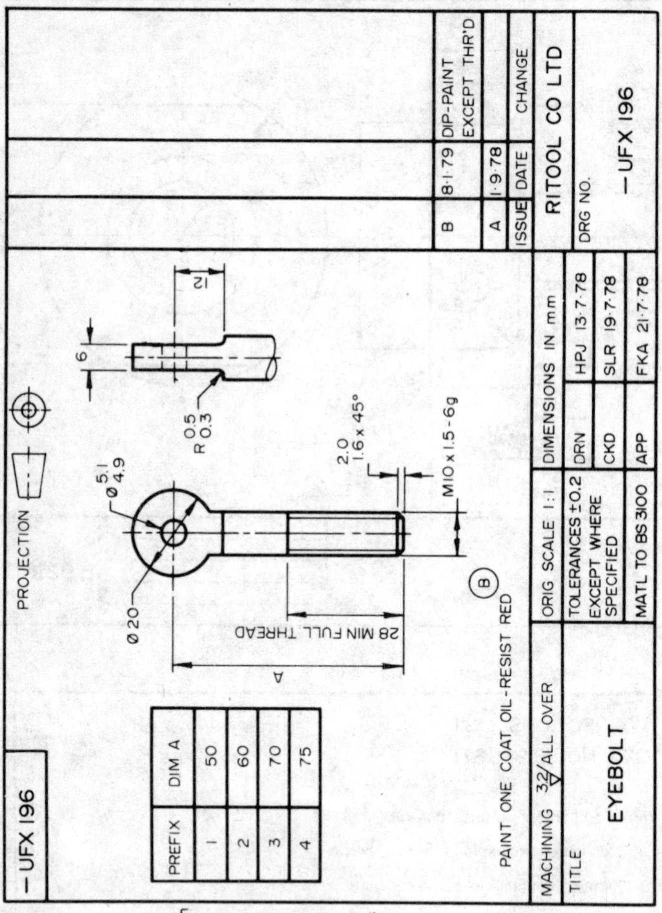

The collective drawing shows four eyebolts which differ only in their length (dimension A). For identification the prefixes 1 to 4 replace the dash before the part number

When the drawing was raised to issue B the paint was deleted from the thread and the painting method was specified as dip-paint

Fig. 1.9 *Collective Detail Drawing Showing Raised Issue*

2 Control of drawing and design work

Drawing office organisation

In order to deal efficiently with the throughput of drawing work, a drawing office needs to be organised into *sections* each having responsibility for part of the work. Figure 2.1 shows a form of organisation suitable for a medium to large drawing office.

Chronological order of drawing and design work

The usual chronological order for drawing and design work, from perception to the finished product, is as follows.

(a) A need for the product is perceived.

(b) A brief, defining the need, is drawn up for the designer's guidance.

(c) The designer researches the problems, interviews clients, refines the brief, prepares and analyses possible solutions, prepares a specification for the product, evaluates possible solutions against the specification and after refining and optimizing, presents the best solution as a scheme.

(d) The scheme is then translated into working detail drawings, sub-assembly drawings, and an assembly drawing.

(e) The drawings are assessed to enable raw material and bought-out items to be ordered, tooling drawings to be prepared, and machines, tools and inspection equipment to be made ready.

(f) Testing arrangements are organised from the assembly drawing or scheme drawings. Rigs may need to be made and prototypes tested.

In order to assist in visualizing what has to be done, several charting methods can be used.

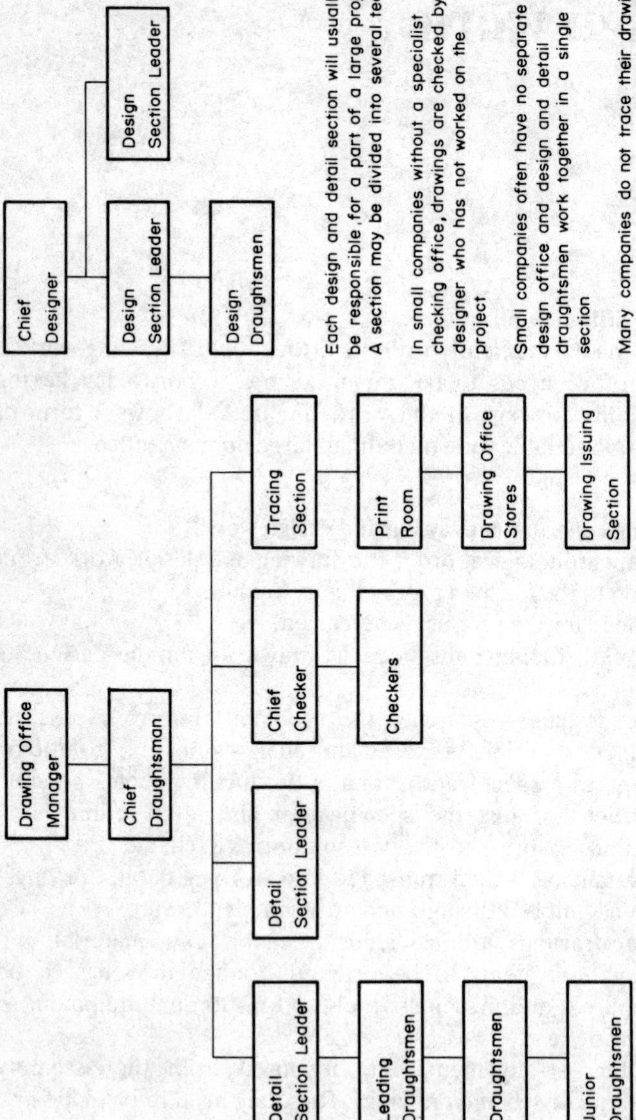

Each design and detail section will usually be responsible for a part of a large project. A section may be divided into several teams

In small companies without a specialist checking office, drawings are checked by a designer who has not worked on the project

Small companies often have no separate design office and design and detail draughtsmen work together in a single section

Many companies do not trace their drawings. Prints are made direct from pencil originals

Fig. 2.1 *Organisation of a Typical Medium to Large Drawing Office*

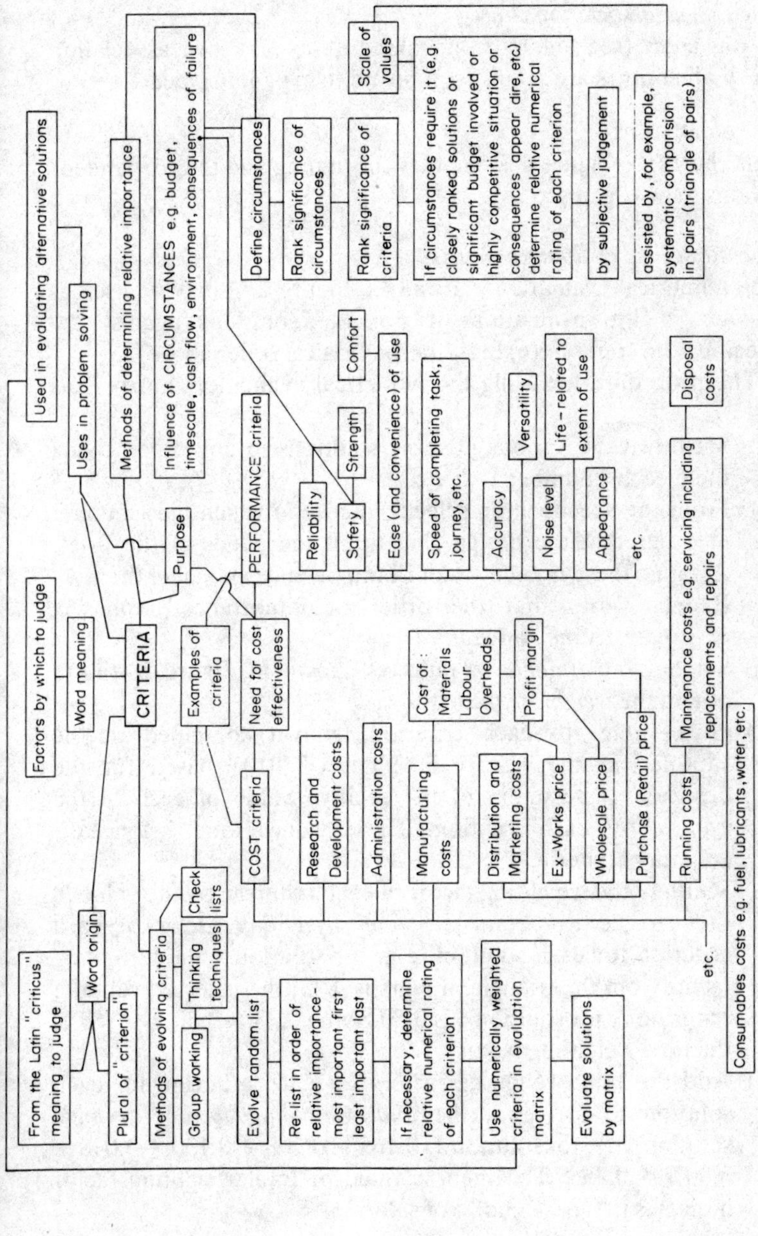

Fig. 2.2 ***Link or Association Chart of Criteria for Problem Solving***

Charting methods

The link or association chart
In this chart (see Figure 2.2), linking items and their association one with another are set down as an aid to expanding ideas.

The block chart
This chart (see Figure 2.3) enables continuing and interdependent actions to be organised.

The numerical evaluation matrix
The numerical evaluation matrix (see Figure 2.4) may be used as an aid in the evaluation of possible solutions against the specification (refer to (c) in the chronological order above).

The procedure for using the numerical evaluation matrix is as follows.

(i) Set down the various possible solutions in any order giving them each a number 1, 2, etc.
(ii) From the specification select the *criteria* which must be met in order that the design shall fulfil the needs of the brief. Arrange these in their order of importance and label them A, B, etc. Note that the order of importance implies a *judgement by the designer*.
(iii) Set out the *triangle of pairs* as shown in Figure 2.4(a) to obtain the *weighting factors*.
(iv) Give *values* to each criterion (shown contained in the capsules in the matrix in Figure 2.4(b)) based on the designer's assessment of the relative value of each of the criteria for each solution. These values total 1 for each column of criteria.
(v) Multiply the weighting factor of each criterion by the value in the capsule to obtain the *final weighting factor* of each criterion for each solution, e.g. for solution 1 the weighting factor from the triangle of pairs is 0.33, the assessed value of criterion A for solution 1 is 0.50 giving $0.33 \times 0.50 = 0.165$ as the final weighting factor.
(vi) Add the final weighting factors for each criterion for each solution to arrive at the *total weighting factor* for each solution, e.g. for solution 1, $0.165 + 0.108 + 0.130 + 0.046 + 0.007 = 0.456$. The highest value of total weighting factor indicates the 'best' choice of solution.

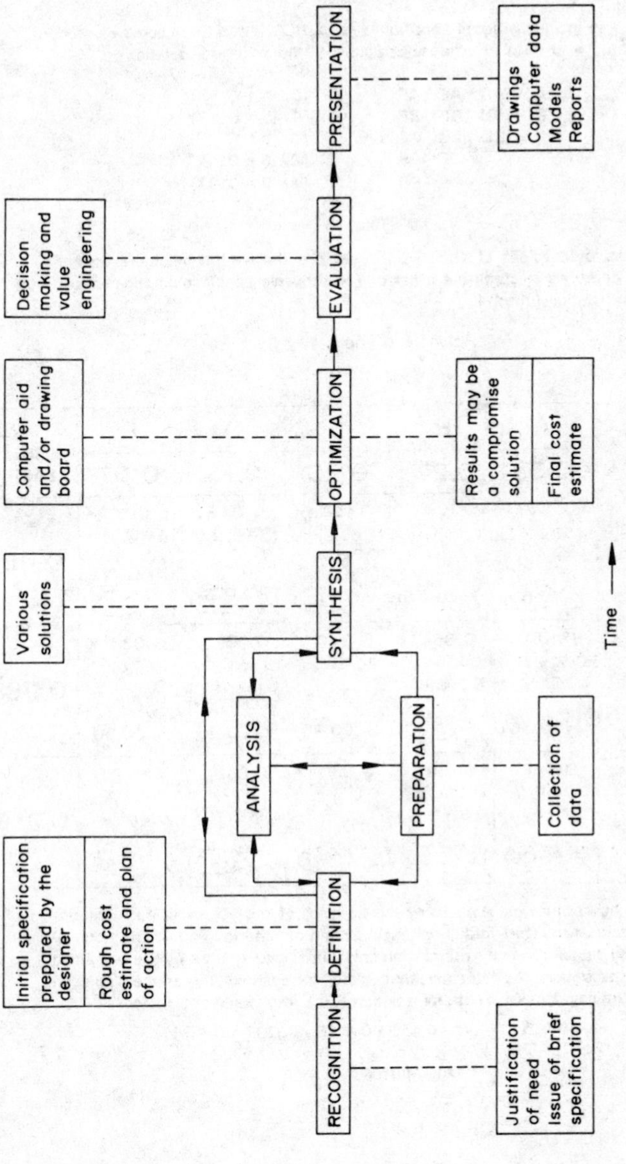

Fig. 2.3 *Block Chart for the Design Process*

List criteria in their order of importance i.e. A, B, C, D and E. A dummy criterion F is added to the list in order to compare all the criteria, as follows:

AB	AC	AD	AE	AF	=	5	(5/15 = 0.33)
	BC	BD	BE	BF	=	4	(4/15 = 0.27)
		CD	CE	CF	=	3	(3/15 = 0.20)
			DE	DF	=	2	(2/15 = 0.13)
				EF	=	1	(1/15 = 0.07)
					Total	15	1.00

The calculated values of 0.33, 0.27, etc are the weighting factors based on the comparison of all the criteria. For convenience of calculation these weighting factors total 1.

(a) Triangle of pairs

CRITERIA / SOLUTIONS	A 0.33	B 0.27	C 0.20	D 0.13	E 0.07	TOTAL WEIGHTING FACTOR
1	0.165 (0.50 x 0.33) (0.50)	0.108 (0.40 x 0.27) (0.40)	0.130 (0.65 x 0.20) (0.65)	0.046 (0.35 x 0.13) (0.35)	0.007 (0.10 x 0.07 (0.10)	0.456
2	0.100 (0.30 x 0.33) (0.30)	0.081 (0.30 x 0.27) (0.30)	0.040 (0.20 x 0.20) (0.20)	0.032 (0.25 x 0.13) (0.25)	0.035 (0.50 x 0.07) (0.50)	0.288
3	0.066 (0.20 x 0.33) (0.20)	0.081 (0.30 x 0.27) (0.30)	0.030 (0.15 x 0.20) (0.15)	0.052 (0.40 x 0.13) (0.40)	0.028 (0.40 x 0.07) (0.40)	0.256

Ringed figures are judgements by the designer of the values of each criterion for each solution. They total 1 for each column of criteria. To find the final weighting factor of each criterion multiply the ringed figures by the weighting factors as shown. The total weighting factor for each solution is the sum of the final weighting factors. Thus, for solution 1, the total weighting factor is

$$0.165 + 0.108 + 0.130 + 0.046 + 0.007 = 0.456$$

(b) Matrix

Fig. 2.4 *Numerical Evaluation Matrix*

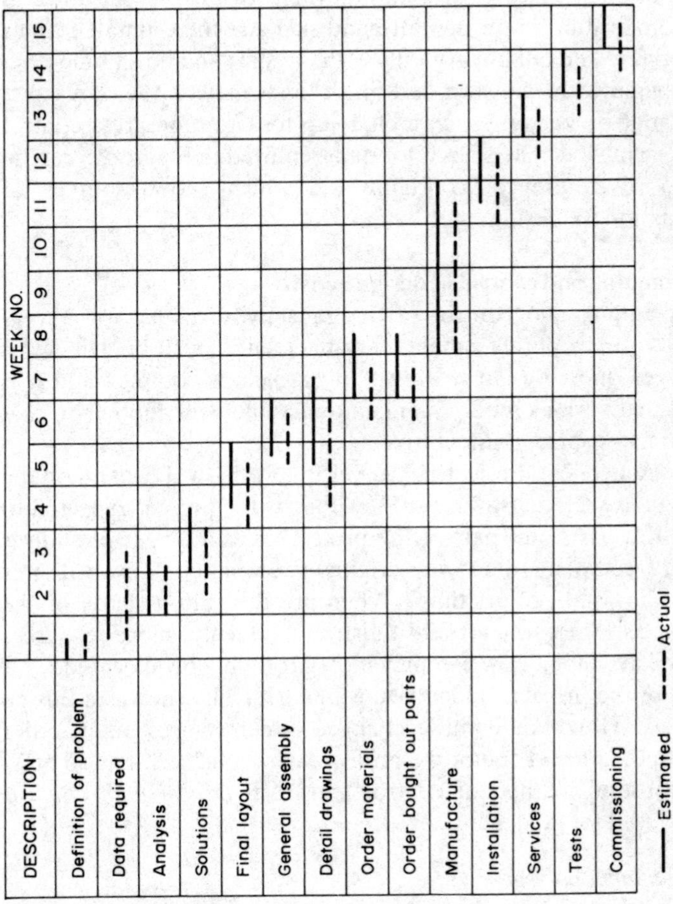

Fig. 2.5 *Bar Chart for Design, Make and Test Programme*

Note that, because various judgements have to be made by the designer, this evaluation is used as an *aid* in the decision process; it can be repeated using different judgements at various stages in an attempt to verify the correctness of the values used.

The bar chart

In the bar chart (see Figure 2.5) all the activities are set down in chronological order on the left-hand side and the estimated times for each are laid out horizontally with the start and finish times.

To begin with, the start and finish times may be the only exact times, but by keeping such a chart up-to-date a progress control can be achieved. The search for data required in Figure 2.5 can be helped by reference to Figure 2.6 which shows sources of information for design.

The planning and control of design activity

The planning and control of design activity might, for a very simple case, be purely a mental arrangement of well-known items. However, most design work on any project is complex and it is found that various requirements interact one with another so that a system of control is imperative.

The control of a project, whatever it may be, will depend on the answers to such questions as: How long is the project expected to take? If a particular part of the project takes a longer or shorter time to complete than was originally estimated, how will this affect the total project time? When are the various parts of the project expected to start and finish? If suddenly, more resources become available, how can they most profitably be allocated, or if a part of the project suddenly runs into difficulty, how can this be handled? How would these changed circumstances affect other parts of the project and/or the project as a whole? . . . and so on.

The useful method of control known as *critical path analysis* can be used for guidance.

Critical path analysis

Some basic definitions have first to be understood. The basic units are the individual parts of the project. These are called *activities* and are represented on the chart by arrows (see Figure 2.7(a)). Activities consume time. The points in time when activities start and stop are called *nodes* (Figure 2.7(b)). They are usually represented on the chart by circles, although other shapes are

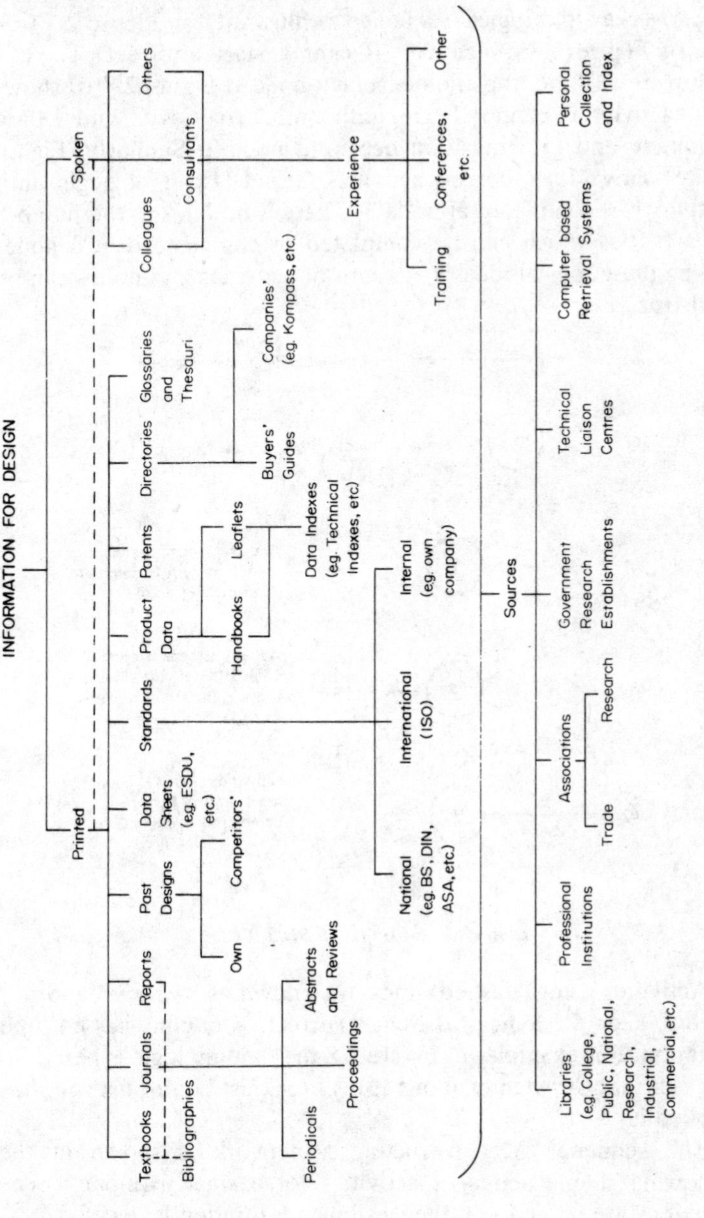

Fig. 2.6 *Sources of Design Information*

sometimes used. They have no time duration but serve to mark the transition points between activities. Activities and nodes are put together in a logical sequence as illustrated in Figure 2.7 (c – e). In Figure 2.7(c), activity B cannot start until activity A is complete and the transition occurs at node 1. Figure 2.7(d) shows that activity E cannot begin until both activities C and D are complete and the transition occurs at node 2. Similarly, Figure 2.7(e) shows that the two activities G and H cannot begin until activity F is completed at node 3. There is no limit to the number of activities which can be completed or commenced at a node. Using these logical ideas a *network* of activities and nodes can be constructed.

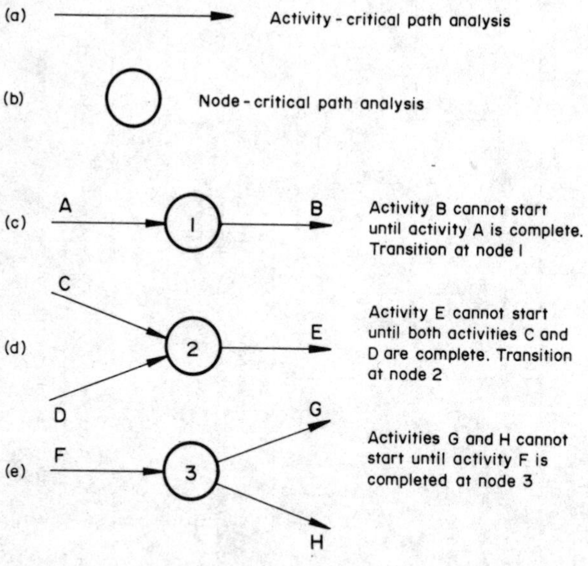

Fig. 2.7 *Activities and Nodes*

Activities using 'dashed' lines are known as *dummies* and are used to keep the logic of the chart correct. A dummy has no time duration. For example, in Figure 2.8 the dummy logic is based on the fact that the man cannot eat his breakfast before his wife has cooked it.

The sequence of constructing a network is shown in the following simple series of activities for a small company. The activities are named and their estimated duration is decided.

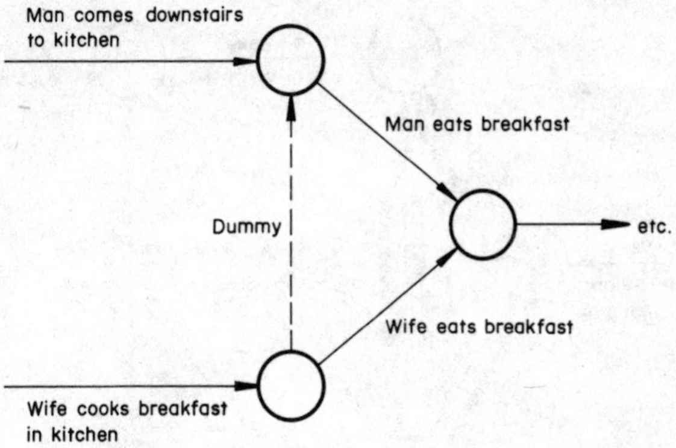

Fig. 2.8 *Use of Dummies*

Scheme drawing and calculations produced (3 weeks)
Detail drawings made (4 weeks)
Prototype built (6 weeks)
Test schedule arranged (1 week)
Prototype tested successfully (4 weeks)
Production schedules arranged (3 weeks)
Tools designed (2 weeks)
Tools made (6 weeks)
Production model built (4 weeks)

The resulting activities and their nodes are set down logically in Figure 2.9. Note that activities which can proceed independently can be shown in parallel (see activities between nodes 4 and 5, and 3 and 6 in Figure 2.9). The activities are shown against the activity lines as well as the times estimated for each activity.

The usefulness of the chart can now be demonstrated and worked through. First the *earliest event times* are arrived at. These are the points in time when the event will occur if all goes according to plan. In the node notation used here, these times are inserted in the bottom left-hand quadrant of the divided node symbol (see Figure 2.10), hence the chart now becomes as shown in Figure 2.10. Thus the earliest event time at node 2 is 3 weeks from node 1, and at node 3 it is 7 weeks, i.e. 3 plus 4. However, at node 4, although the activities 1 to 2 and 2 to 4 add up to 4 weeks, the earliest event time is actually 13 weeks because activities 2 to 3 and 3 to 4 impose a penalty of 10 weeks. Likewise, using the earliest event time at node 4 plus 4 weeks from 4 to 5 gives an

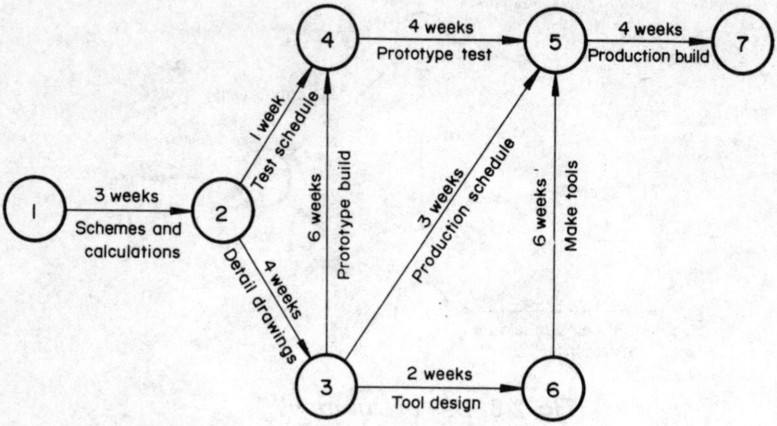

Fig. 2.9 *Activities, Nodes and Estimated Times*

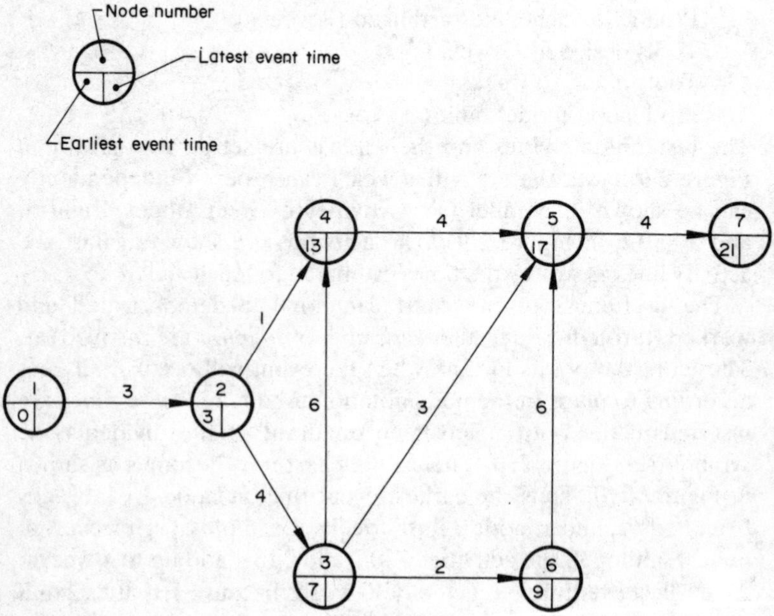

Fig. 2.10 *Earliest Event Times*

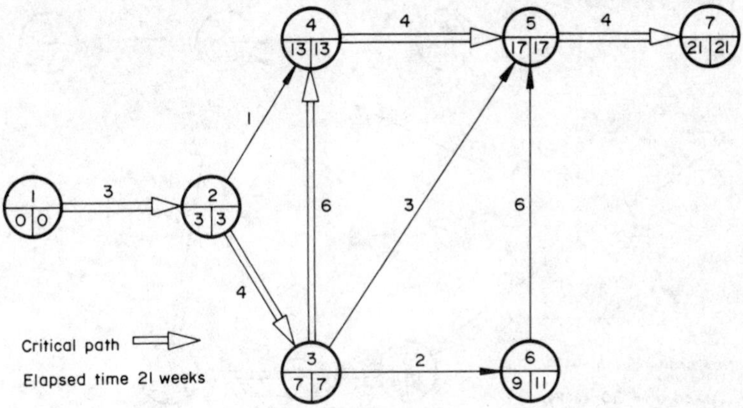

Fig. 2.11 *Latest Event Times and Critical Path*

earliest event time at node 5 of 17 weeks. Adding activity 3 to 5 to the earliest event time at node 3 or adding activity 3 to 6 and activity 6 to 5 would give earliest event times at node 5 less than 17 weeks.

Now the *latest event times* (see Figure 2.11) can be entered in a similar fashion in the bottom right-hand quadrants of the node symbols. To evaluate these latest event times it is necessary to work *backwards* from the end time of the project; so that, for example, the latest event time at node 6 is 17 minus 6 = 11 weeks from the start of the project.

Now it is possible to see the critical timing or *critical path* where there is no slack time or 'float' at the nodes. So, in Figure 2.11, the critical path, designated by double lines, lies from nodes 1 to 2 to 3 to 4 to 5 to 7 and the total *elapsed time* will be 21 weeks.

From the earliest and latest event times at node 6, it can be seen that either the tool design time can be extended by 2 weeks or the tool making time can be extended; both activities could release draughtspersons or tool makers for other activities.

Now imagine that 7 weeks from the starting date, part of the factory where tool design and manufacture is carried out is seriously damaged by fire and the design and making of the tools has to be contracted out. The search for a suitable contractor takes 2 weeks, followed by the contractor taking 4 weeks over the design of the tools and 6 weeks to make and deliver them. The network can be redrawn to show a changed critical path (see Figure 2.12) so despite the search for a tooling contractor and his

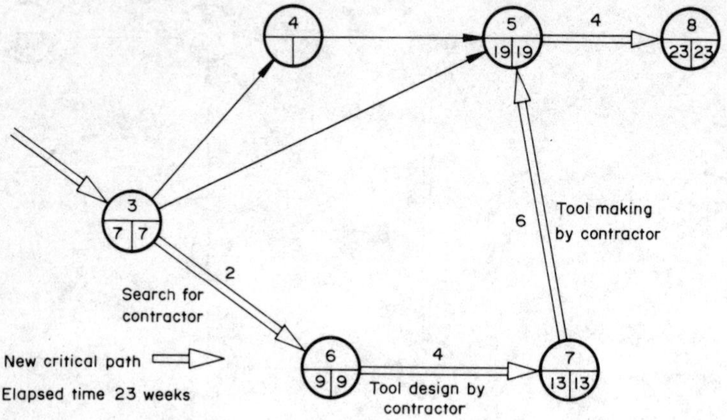

Fig. 2.12 *New Critical Path*

longer tool design time (because he has to fit it in with other work), the total elapsed time has only increased by 2 weeks. However, the critical path is now intimately linked with another company who, it is hoped, will deliver on time! Also it is possible to allow more time for the prototype build and testing, although it would have been sensible in any case to reckon with possible delays in these activities.

This chapter has pointed out how critical a factor is time spent on a project which includes design. Any way by which the designer's time can be cut is worth consideration, for example, reference should be made to current British Standards which are listed in the Institution's annual catalogue. This will avoid redesigning parts or creating parts which are already available. In addition it will ensure that standardized limits and fits, with their associated drills and reamers, are used. Standardized symbols, requirements and methods of test can be used which will save time and therefore money and avoid errors. Useful further reading will be found in BS 6046, BS 4335 and in Engineering Teaching Aids published by the Design Council.

It may be said in conclusion that in many cases no one thing alone provides the crux of a design. In practice each new deliberation will probably require some sort of modification of the gradually evolving design which, in turn, requires a change to the scheme drawing. Therefore there is no substitute for a clear and readable drawing as a means of communication.

3 Dimensioning and tolerancing

Principles of dimensioning

These principles are described in detail in BS 308: Part 2 Dimensioning and tolerancing of size. For a full coverage of the principles, the reader should consult that standard; those that follow are the more important.

All dimensions, tolerances and information necessary for the complete description and satisfactory functioning of the part should be expressed directly on the drawing and appear once only. Dimensions should be given to the least number of significant figures, e.g. 35 and not 35.0. Note that it is recommended that dimensions should be placed on the dimension line, as in Figure 3.1(a), rather than in the dimension line, as in Figure 3.1(b).

Fig. 3.1 *Dimension and Dimension Line*

Dimensions should show the part in the condition in which it is to be used. This means that the drawing may define the part as ready for assembly or service, or as the product of a foundry, forge, etc., supplied for finishing by machining.

Dimensions should be placed on the view which shows the relevant features most clearly. Examples of the application of this principle are shown in Figure 3.2.

Preferred sizes of holes, thread forms, screw fasteners, pins, etc., and standard material sizes should be used wherever practical.

No more dimensions should be given than are necessary to describe the part. This means that a feature should be located by only one dimension in any one direction.

Production processes, such as drill, ream, mill, etc., and inspection methods should not be specified unless they are essential for satisfactory functioning or interchangeability.

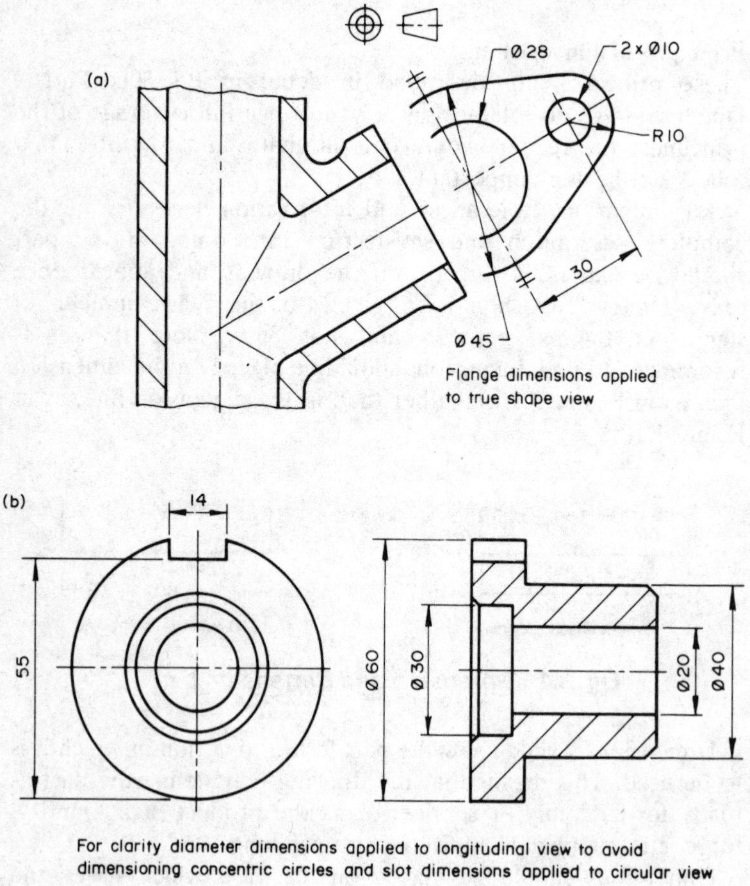
(a)
Ø28
2 x Ø10
R10
30
Ø45
Flange dimensions applied to true shape view
(b)
14
55
Ø60
Ø30
Ø20
Ø40
For clarity diameter dimensions applied to longitudinal view to avoid dimensioning concentric circles and slot dimensions applied to circular view

Fig. 3.2 *Dimensions Applied to Best View for Clarity*

Functional dimensioning
The satisfactory dimensioning of a detail drawing requires that the dimensions chosen define the part completely and unambiguously, without the need for the workshop to make calculations or to refer doubtful points to the designer for clarification. Equally, however, satisfactory dimensioning requires that those dimensions which are essential to the correct functioning of the part, called *functional dimensions*, are stated directly on the drawing. The remaining non-functional dimensions can be chosen to aid the production or inspection of the part.

Stating functional dimensions directly on the drawing means that *datum features* will be chosen on the basis of the function of the part and how it is located in the assembly. The design scheme will show the arrangement of the assembled parts and from it the functionally important features, i.e. the datum features, can be deduced. A datum feature is generally a face, edge or axis and the functional dimensions of the part originate from it. Two simple examples of the application of functional dimensioning are shown in Figure 3.3.

It is important to understand that if a datum feature is chosen which is not based on the function of the part, smaller tolerances will automatically be necessary on the functional dimensions. This may mean that parts which would satisfy the functional requirements of the assembly will be rejected because they exceed those smaller tolerances.

Sometimes, however, a datum feature chosen to satisfy the functional requirements may be inconvenient for machining or inspection requirements. In such cases the workshop may decide to use a different datum feature and accept the resulting smaller tolerances in the interests of easier machining or inspection.

Drawings for parts to be made on numerically controlled machines are often dimensioned from a common datum point to suit the operation of the machine. Smaller tolerances will again result because the functional datum features are not used, but the accuracy of these machines is such that usually the smaller tolerances can be met.

Tolerancing
No manufactured part is ever quite the same as those which precede or follow it in a batch because of inherent inaccuracies in

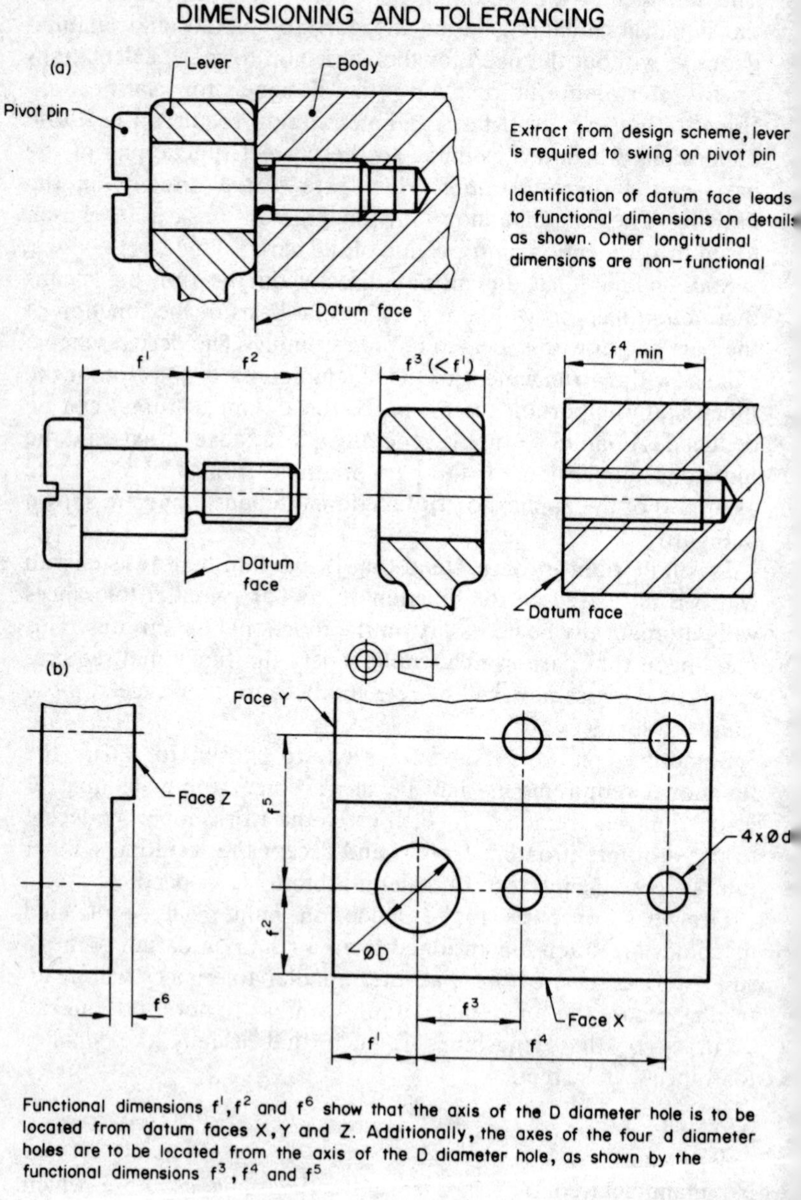
DIMENSIONING AND TOLERANCING
(a)
Lever
Body
Pivot pin
Extract from design scheme, lever is required to swing on pivot pin
Identification of datum face leads to functional dimensions on details as shown. Other longitudinal dimensions are non-functional
Datum face
f¹
f²
f³ (<f¹)
f⁴ min
Datum face
Datum face
(b)
Face Y
Face Z
f⁵
4 x Ød
f²
ØD
f⁶
f³
Face X
f¹
f⁴
Functional dimensions f¹, f² and f⁶ show that the axis of the D diameter hole is to be located from datum faces X, Y and Z. Additionally, the axes of the four d diameter holes are to be located from the axis of the D diameter hole, as shown by the functional dimensions f³, f⁴ and f⁵

Fig. 3.3 *Functional Dimensioning*

the machine or process, tool wear, temperature changes, operator variance and so on. Therefore the designer has to prescribe the maximum and minimum sizes for dimensions that will enable the part to function satisfactorily. The difference between the maximum and minimum sizes is the permitted variation for the dimension and is called the *tolerance*. It may be expressed on the drawing in two ways, as illustrated in Figure 3.4. The two methods are equally applicable to angular dimensions.

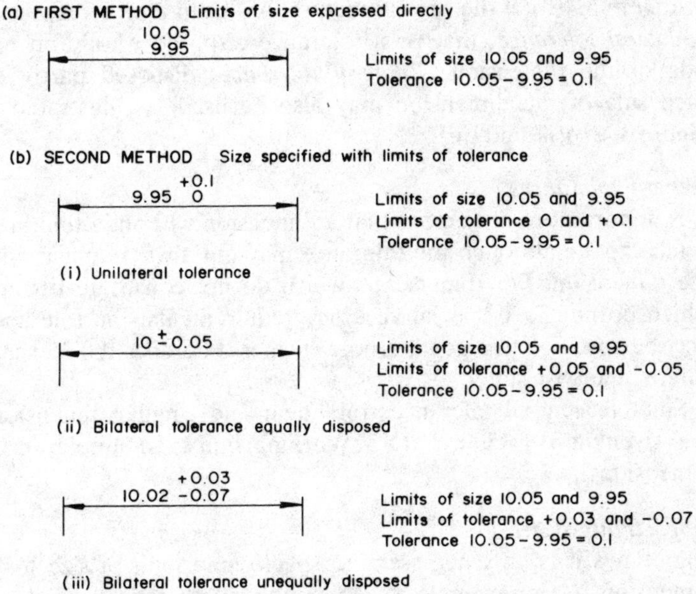

Fig. 3.4 *Tolerancing of Linear Dimensions*

In the first method, shown in Figure 3.4(a), the maximum and minimum sizes, or *limits of size*, are specified directly. The larger limit of size should be placed above the smaller and both should be given to the same number of decimal places.

In the second method, shown in Figure 3.4(b), a size is specified with *limits of tolerance* above and below that size. Both limits of tolerance should have the same number of decimal places except when one limit is nil when it should be written as '0', without a plus or minus sign. It is not necessary to give the dimension to the same number of decimal places as the limits of tolerance. As with the first method, the limit of tolerance which produces the larger limit of size should be placed above that which produces the smaller limit of size.

There is no difference in the interpretations of the two methods, each of which does no more than define the maximum and minimum limits of size. However, specifying the limits of size directly, as in Figure 3.4(a), avoids the workman having to calculate them from the dimension and the limits of tolerance.

Unilateral and bilateral tolerances

In Figure 3.4(b)(i) the second method has been used to express a *unilateral tolerance*, that is, a tolerance disposed wholly on one side of the dimension. *Bilateral tolerances* disposed partly on each side of the dimension may also be used, as illustrated in Figure 3.4(b)(ii) and (iii).

General tolerances

It is important to remember that a dimension without a tolerance is incomplete although the tolerance may not always appear with the dimension. For dimensions which do not constitute fits and which do not have special accuracy requirements, the tolerance may be specified in a general note such as 'tolerance ±0.2 except where otherwise stated'.

Suitable general tolerances for linear and angular dimensions are given in BS 4500: Part 3 Working limits on untoleranced dimensions.

Single limits of size

Sometimes it is only necessary to specify one limit of size for a dimension, as, for example, the minimum length of full thread in a tapped hole or the maximum size of a radius permitted at a corner. In such cases the abbreviation 'MIN' or 'MAX' should follow the dimension.

Cumulative effects of tolerances

Where *chain dimensioning* of toleranced centre distances is used, the tolerances may have a cumulative effect, as in Figure 3.5(a). Here the tolerances on the distances from the plate edge to the axes of the holes A, B and C are, respectively, ±0.2, ±0.4, and ±0.6.

One way of reducing this accumulation is to use *parallel dimensioning* from a common datum, the plate edge, as in Figure 3.5(b). Now all three hole axes have a tolerance of ±0.2 relative to

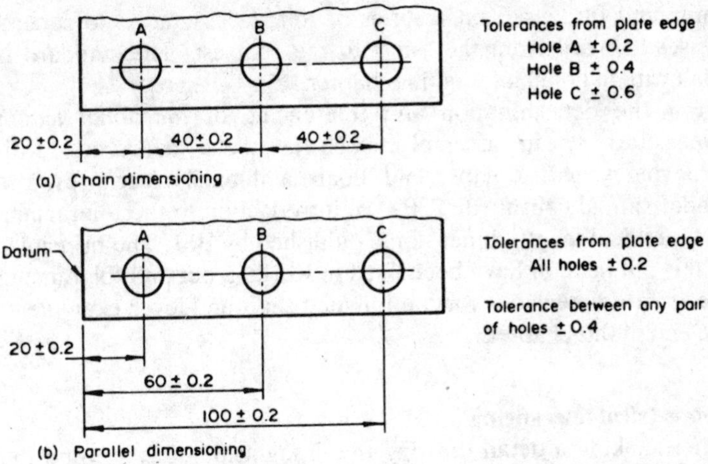

Fig. 3.5 *Cumulative Effects of Tolerances*

the plate edge. However, the tolerance between hole axes A and B, B and C, and A and C is ±0.4.

The use of *positional tolerances* for the hole axes will also avoid the accumulation of tolerances. Chain dimensioning can then be used, employing theoretically exact or boxed dimensions between the axes. In general, the use of positional tolerances should be considered whenever two or more features need to be related together as a group. This is dealt with later in the section on geometrical tolerancing.

Size of tolerances

Beginners often find it difficult to decide what size of tolerance they should use and this leads to tolerances being applied which are smaller than necessary. In all cases the largest tolerance consistent with satisfactory functioning of the part should be used. The cost of production of a part is directly related to the sizes of the tolerances, since small tolerances will usually require more skill from the machine operator, more frequent resetting of the machine because of tool wear and more time for the completion of the part. Furthermore, small tolerances will often dictate the use of a particular machine or process, whereas if the tolerances were relaxed it might be possible to use an alternative simpler machine or cheaper process.

BS 4500 ISO limits and fits provides a comprehensive range of limits and fits based on a series of tolerances graded to suit all classes of work from the finest to the coarsest. The standard is dealt with in detail later in this chapter.

For the determination and tolerancing of *functional length dimensions* in an assembly, such as those concerned with achieving specified gaps, end floats and axial clearances, the reader should consult PP 7309 An introduction to the tolerancing of functional length dimensions, published by BSI. The principles in this publication have been used in working out and tolerancing the length dimensions for the tongued shaft and lever example at the end of this chapter.

Geometrical tolerancing

When making a detail drawing the draughtsman has in mind the ideal or perfect form of the features of the part and their perfect relationship to each other. However, he knows that the dimensions of the features cannot be manufactured to exact sizes. Therefore he specifies upper and lower limits of size for the dimensions such that parts made to them will function satisfactorily.

Equally, the geometry of the features will not be perfect. For example, a cylindrical pin will not be perfectly round neither will its axis be perfectly straight. If the pin has a cylindrical head, the head and shank will not be perfectly coaxial.

It may be necessary to control deviations from true geometry if the part is to meet its functional requirements. A degree of control can be exercised by the limits of size specified for the features, by requiring that if a feature is at its maximum material limit of size, it shall be perfect in form. The maximum material limit of size is the one at which the feature contains the maximum amount of material. For an external feature, such as a pin, it is the high limit of size; for an internal feature, such as a hole, it is the low limit of size. At the maximum material limit of size a feature is said to be in its *maximum material condition* (MMC). So the maximum material limit of size establishes a boundary of perfect form for the feature. If the feature is not at its maximum material size it is permitted to have form errors. Such errors must not allow the finished surfaces of the feature to cross the maximum material boundary of perfect form and the feature must be within the specified limits of size.

In some circumstances the limits of size for the feature may permit form deviations that are too large to be functionally acceptable. In this event *geometrical tolerances* of form should be specified and these take precedence over the form control implied by the limits of size.

Geometrical tolerancing is dealt with in detail by BS 308: Part 3 Geometrical tolerancing and in PD 7304 Introduction to geometrical tolerancing, both published by the British Standards Institution. Only the basic principles of the subject are covered here and for a full treatment the reader should consult those publications.

When geometrical tolerances are used

Geometrical tolerances should be specified for all requirements critical to functioning and interchangeability except when it is known that the machinery and manufacturing techniques that will be used can be relied on to achieve the required standard of accuracy. Their use will permit the satisfactory functioning and interchangeability of parts made in different locations, on varying equipment and by personnel with varying experience.

Geometrical tolerances should be specified only where they are essential, otherwise the manufacturing and inspection costs of parts will be increased. In any case the tolerances should be as wide as possible, subject to the design requirements being met.

Definition of geometrical tolerance

A geometrical tolerance defines the size and shape of a *tolerance zone* within which the feature is to lie. It represents the full indicator movement (FIM) where testing with an indicator is applicable, e.g. a run-out tolerance (see Figure 3.21). A geometrical tolerance applies to the whole extent of a feature unless a more restrictive requirement is specified.

Features of a part and their characteristics

Figure 3.6 illustrates some of the *features* that may be present on a part. Features have *characteristics*, for example, an axis has the characteristic of being straight; a cylinder has the characteristic of being round; and a face has the characteristic of being flat. Geometrical tolerances limit the deviations from true geometry of the characteristics.

Symbols are used on drawings to denote characteristics. This avoids using words which may not be understood outside the

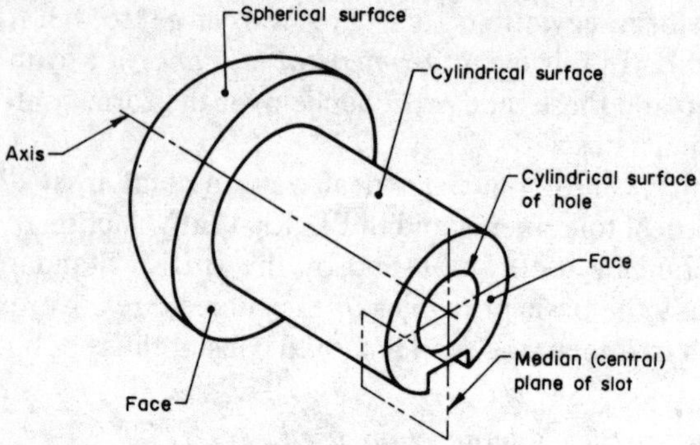

Fig. 3.6 *Features of a Part*

country of origin of the drawing. The symbols are shown in Figure 3.7 and fall into two main groups. The first comprises characteristics for single features. The characteristics in the second group apply to related features. For example, a feature toleranced for squareness needs to be referred to a second feature (a datum) to which the squareness is to be assessed. Characteristics for related features fall into subgroups for attitude, location and composite tolerances.

	TYPE OF TOLERANCE	CHARACTERISTIC TO BE TOLERANCED	SYMBOL
For single features	Form	Straightness	—
		Flatness	▱
		Roundness	○
		Cylindricity	⌭
		Profile of a line	⌒
		Profile of a surface	⌓
For related features	Attitude	Parallelism	//
		Squareness	⊥
		Angularity	∠
	Location	Position	⌖
		Concentricity	◎
		Symmetry	⌯
	Composite	Run-out	↗

Fig. 3.7 *Symbols for Toleranced Characteristics*

Indications on drawings

Boxed dimensions

Boxed dimensions show theoretically exact positions, profiles and angles. They are not given size tolerances and the enclosing boxes are drawn with thin lines, see Figure 3.8. Boxed dimensions locate tolerance zones, the boundaries of which are given by the geometrical tolerances of position, profile and angularity. They are not used with any other characteristics.

Fig. 3.8 *Boxed Dimensions*

Tolerance frame

Geometrical tolerances are shown in rectangular *tolerance frames* which are divided into compartments as shown in Figure 3.9(a). Frames are drawn with thin lines.

In the left-hand compartment the symbol for the characteristic being toleranced is given. The next compartment contains the total geometrical tolerance in the units used for linear dimensions. If the tolerance zone is circular or cylindrical the tolerance value is preceded by the symbol ø.

When a datum feature or datum system has to be identified, the third and succeeding compartments contain the datum identification letters.

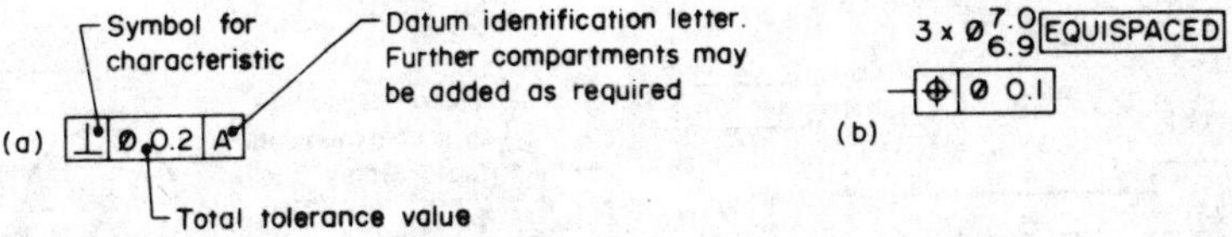

Fig. 3.9 *Tolerance Frame*

Other information relating to the feature should preferably be placed above the tolerance frame as in Figure 3.9(b).

Leader from tolerance frame

A leader from the tolerance frame (see Figure 3.10) connects the tolerance frame with the feature controlled by the tolerance. The leader arrowhead touches the controlled feature. The width of the geometrical tolerance zone for the controlled feature lies in the

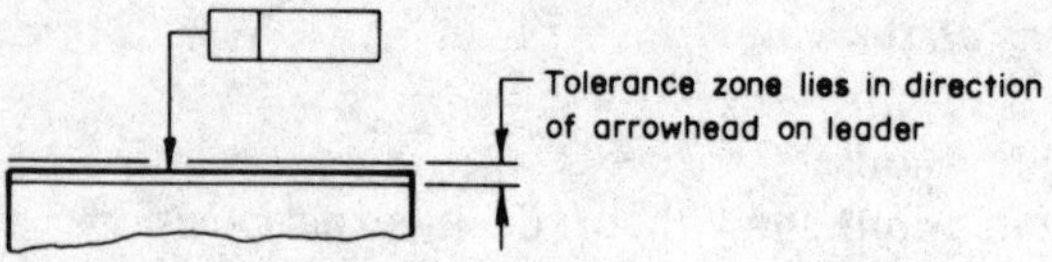

Fig. 3.10 *Leader from Tolerance Frame*

direction of the arrowhead. Therefore the angle at which the leader touches the controlled feature is important and is usually at right-angles to the controlled feature.

Position of leader arrowhead

The position of the leader arrowhead has considerable significance and the differences in meaning between the positions shown in Figures 3.11(a), (b) and (c) should be carefully noted.

Figure 3.11(a). When the arrowhead touches the outline, or an extension of the outline *but not at a dimension line*, the tolerance refers to the surface, face, edge or line touched by the arrowhead.

Figure 3.11(b). When the arrowhead is positioned at a dimension line the tolerance refers to the axis or median plane of the dimensioned feature only.

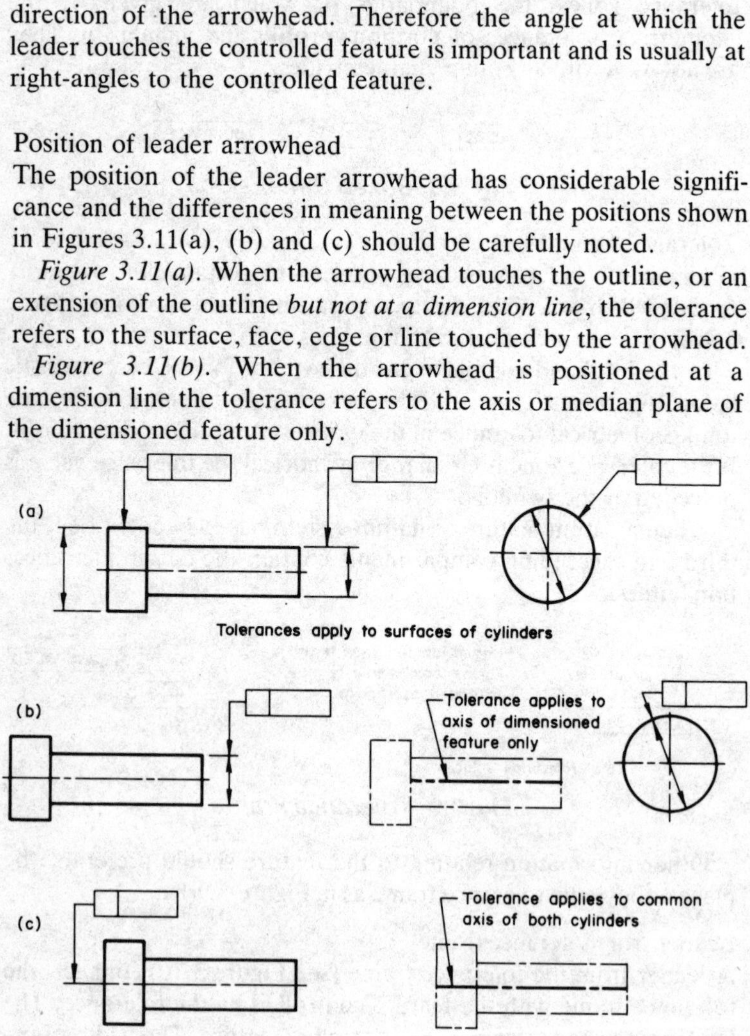

Fig. 3.11 *Position of Leader Arrowhead*

Figure 3.11(c). When the arrowhead is positioned on the axis or median plane the tolerance refers to the common axis or median plane of all the features on that axis or median plane.

Datums and datum features

A *datum* is a theoretically exact geometric reference, such as an axis, plane or straight line, to which toleranced features are related. A *datum feature* is a real feature of a part, such as an edge, a flat or cylindrical surface, which is used to establish the location of a datum. More than one datum feature may be needed to establish a datum.

Figure 3.12(a) shows how a datum feature is indicated. A leader from the tolerance frame terminates in a triangle which shows the controlling or datum feature. To avoid long leaders the method shown in Figure 3.12(b) may be used. Here the datum feature is identified by a capital letter in a frame and the same letter appears in the third compartment of the tolerance frame.

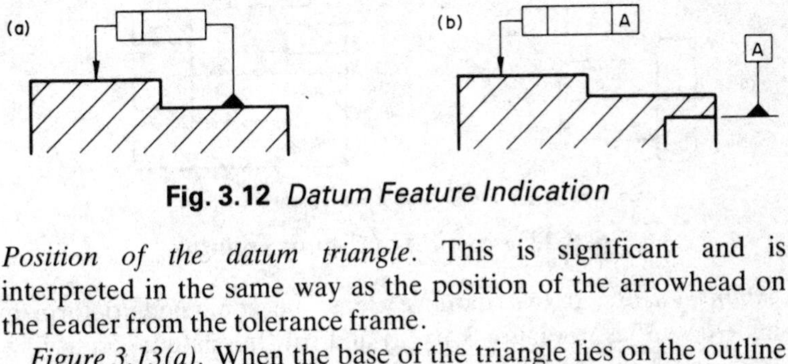

Fig. 3.12 *Datum Feature Indication*

Position of the datum triangle. This is significant and is interpreted in the same way as the position of the arrowhead on the leader from the tolerance frame.

Figure 3.13(a). When the base of the triangle lies on the outline or extension of the outline of the feature, *but not at a dimension line*, the datum feature is the line or surface itself.

Figures 3.13(b) and (c). When the base of the triangle lies on the outline or projection line at a dimension line, the datum is the axis or median plane of the dimensioned feature only.

Figure 3.13(d). When the base of the triangle lies on the axis or median plane, the datum is the common axis or median plane of all the features on that axis or median plane.

Accuracy of datums. Datum features must be sufficiently accurate for their purpose. Therefore it may be necessary to apply form or position tolerances, or both, to a feature to be used as a datum. Figure 3.14 illustrates this principle.

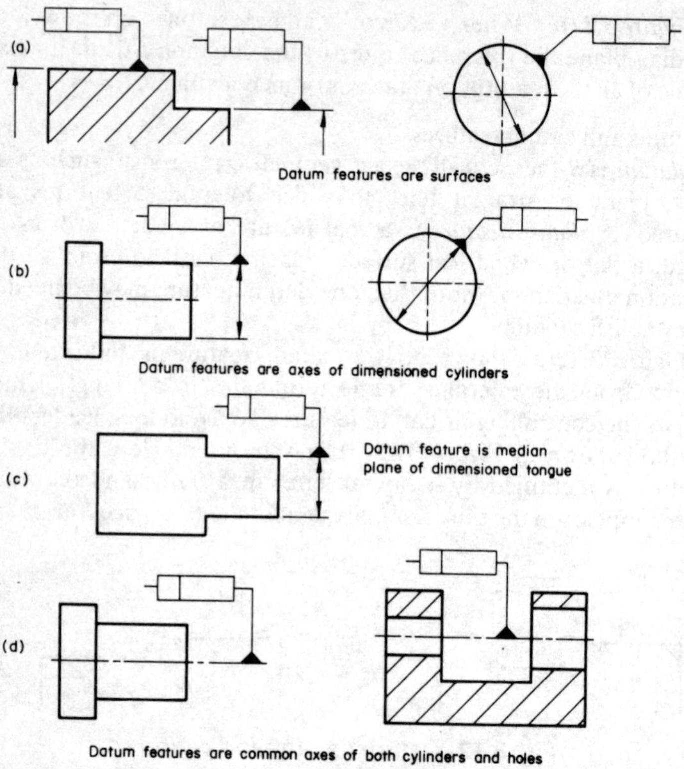
(a)
Datum features are surfaces
(b)
Datum features are axes of dimensioned cylinders
(c)
Datum feature is median plane of dimensioned tongue
(d)
Datum features are common axes of both cylinders and holes

Fig. 3.13 *Position of Datum Triangle*

Datum systems. If two datums are to be combined to form a single datum as in Figure 3.15 (a) and (b), the datum identifying letters in the tolerance frame are separated by a hyphen.

When the datum identification letters for a multiple datum system appear together in one compartment of the tolerance frame, the datums may be applied in any order in manufacture or inspection (see Figure 3.15(c)).

If the datums making up a multiple datum system have to be applied in a particular order, then that order of priority is shown from left to right in the tolerance frame (see Figure 3.15(d)).

Tolerance applied to a restricted part of a feature
If a tolerance is applicable to a restricted part of a feature, the part of the feature controlled by the tolerance is shown as a thick chain line, as in Figure 3.16.

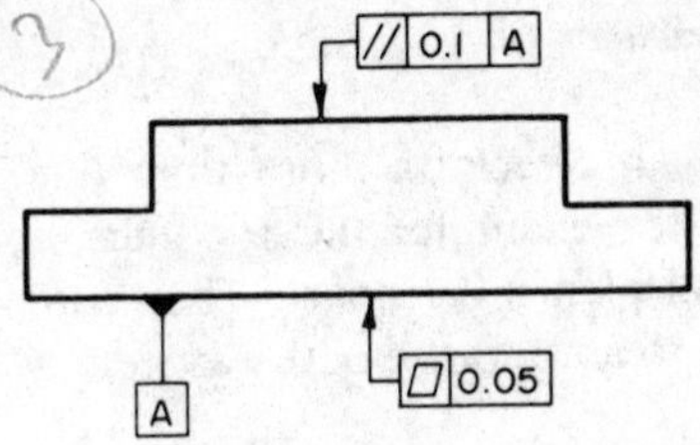

Flatness tolerance applied to lower surface to ensure it is sufficiently accurate to be used as a datum to control the parallelism of the upper surface

(a)

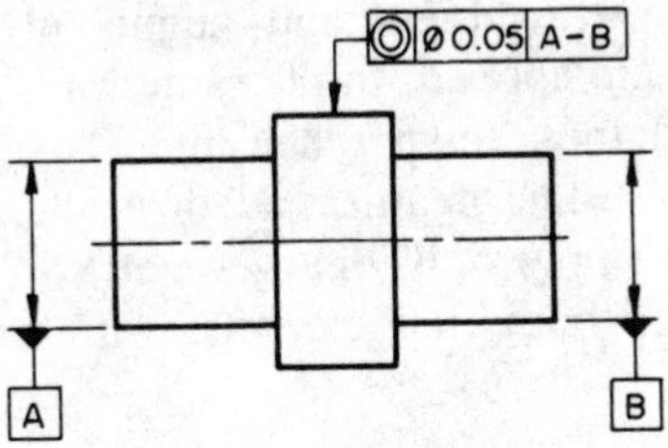

A–B means that datum axes A and B are to be combined to form a single datum to control the concentricity of the central portion

(b)

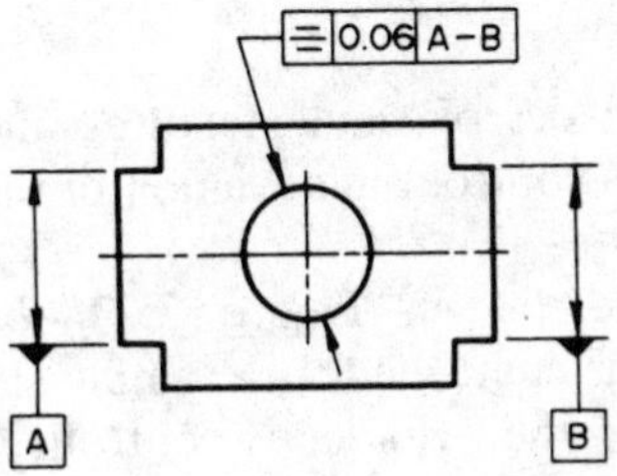

A–B means that datum median planes A and B are to be combined to form a single datum to control the symmetry of the hole axis

(c)

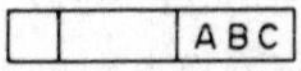

When the datum identification letters appear together in one compartment the datums may be taken in any order

(d)

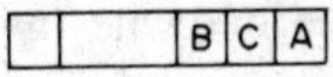

Datum identification letters in separate compartments show, from left to right, the order of priority of the datums

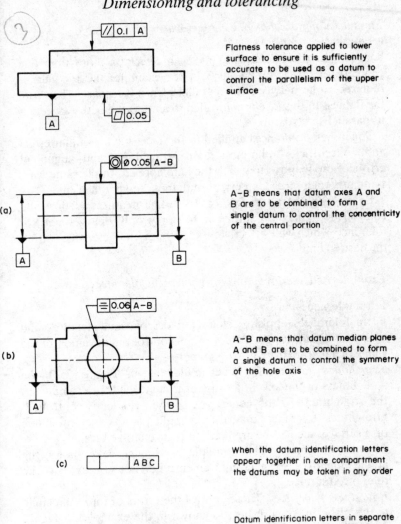

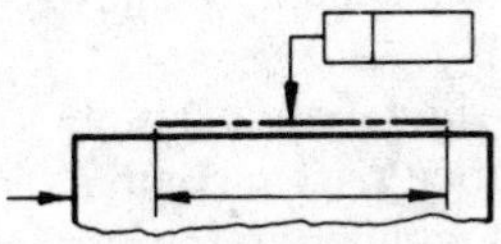

The thick chain line shows the part of the feature to which the tolerance is to apply

Fig. 3.16 *Tolerance Applied to Restricted Part of Feature*

Limitation of more than one geometrical error by a single geometrical tolerance

Some geometrical tolerances have an effect on more than one geometrical error. In Figure 3.14 for example, the top face is required to lie between two parallel planes 0.1 apart. Therefore the flatness of this face is controlled to a tolerance of 0.1 as well as its parallelism to datum A.

Squareness tolerances applied to flat faces have a similar effect and concentricity tolerances limit straightness and alignment errors of the features to which they are applied. In the same way, symmetry tolerances limit errors of flatness and parallelism.

So if two characteristics of the same feature need to be controlled, it may be sufficient to apply only one geometrical tolerance which will effectively keep both characteristics within the desired limits.

Examples and interpretations of geometrical tolerances

Form tolerances

Form tolerances apply to characteristics of single features and therefore do not need a datum. They control the deviation of the shape of a feature from its true shape.

Straightness tolerances. In example (a) in Figure 3.17 the straightness of the axis of a cylinder is controlled. In example (b) the straightness of the generators of the cylinder is controlled. Straightness tolerances may also be applied to an edge or to a line on a surface, such as the graduations of an engraved scale.

Flatness tolerances. The example in Figure 3.17 shows the application of a special requirement, i.e. not concave, to the toleranced surface.

Roundness tolerances. These control the errors of form of a circle in the plane in which it lies, as shown in the examples in Figure 3.17. Roundness tolerances are not concerned with the position of the circle, for example its concentricity with an axis. The roundness of each circular cross-section has to be assessed separately, the cross-sections being established by planes at right-angles to the axis.

Cylindricity tolerances. Figure 3.18 shows an example of the application of this tolerance. Cylindricity is a combination of roundness, straightness and parallelism applied to the surface of a cylinder. It might seem convenient to use a cylindricity tolerance

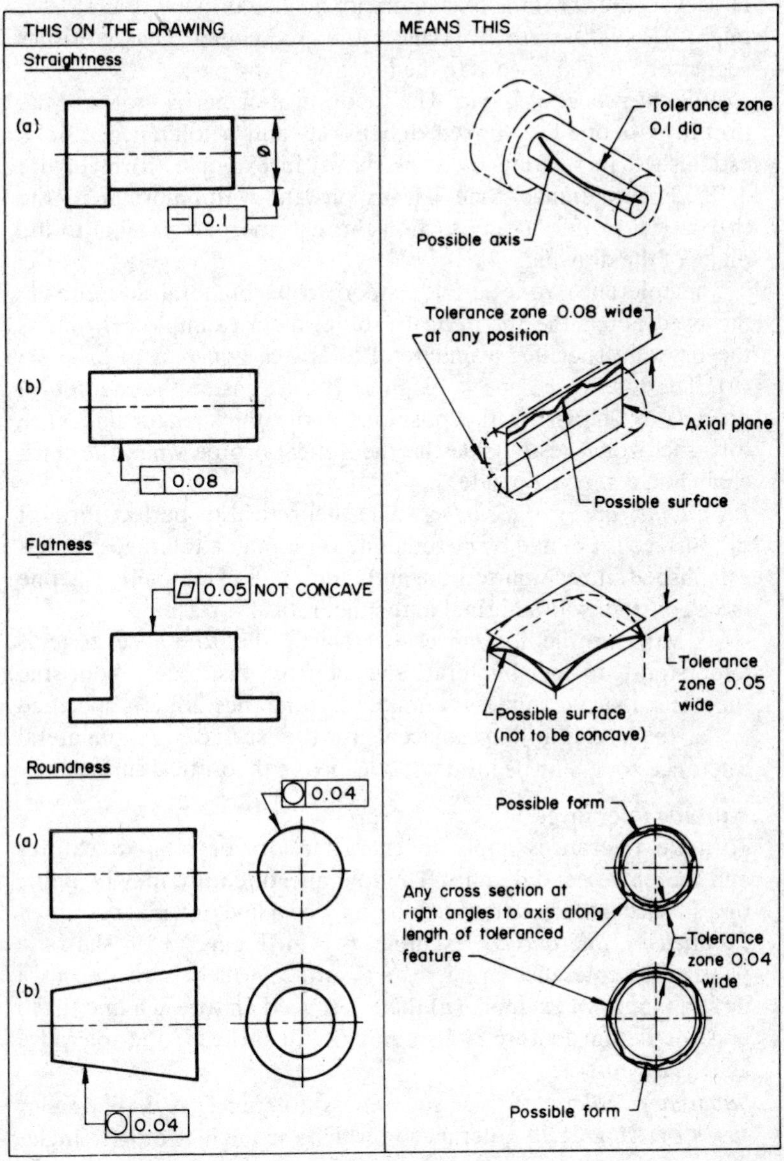

Fig. 3.17 *Examples and Interpretations of Geometrical Tolerances*

to control simultaneously the errors in these three characteristics. However, the checking of cylindricity may be difficult, therefore it might be better to tolerance the individual characteristics separately, having regard to the function of the part.

Profile tolerances of a line. The theoretical or perfect form of the profile is defined by boxed dimensions and a tolerance zone is established in relation to it, as shown in example (a) in Figure 3.18. The tolerance zone has a constant width normal to the theoretical profile in any section through the part parallel to the plane of the drawing.

The tolerance zone is understood to be bilateral and equally disposed about the theoretical profile, as in example (a), unless the drawing specifies a unilateral tolerance zone, as in example (b). The tolerance zone in example (b) lies inside the theoretical profile, as shown by the position of the thick chain line. The tolerance zone lies outside the theoretical profile when the thick chain line is shown outside.

Profile tolerances of a surface. The theoretical or perfect form of the surface is defined by boxed dimensions and a tolerance zone is established in relation to it, as in Figure 3.18. The tolerance zone has a constant width normal to the theoretical surface.

As with profile tolerances of a line, the tolerance zone is understood to be bilateral and equally disposed about the theoretical surface unless a unilateral tolerance zone is specified by a thick chain line adjacent to the surface. A unilateral tolerance zone may be inside or outside the theoretical surface.

Attitude tolerances

Attitude tolerances apply to characteristics of related features and therefore need datums. The toleranced feature may be a line or a surface and the datum feature may be a line or a plane.

Parallelism tolerances. Example (a) in Figure 3.19 shows a parallelism tolerance applied to a surface which is related to a datum plane. In example (b) the toleranced feature is a line (axis) and the datum feature is also an axis. In this case the tolerance zone is a cylinder.

Squareness tolerances. A squareness tolerance is a particular case of an angularity tolerance in which the angle is a right-angle. In example (a) in Figure 3.19 the toleranced feature is a surface and the datum feature is a plane. In example (b) in Figure 3.19 the toleranced feature is an axis with a cylindrical tolerance zone and the datum feature is a plane.

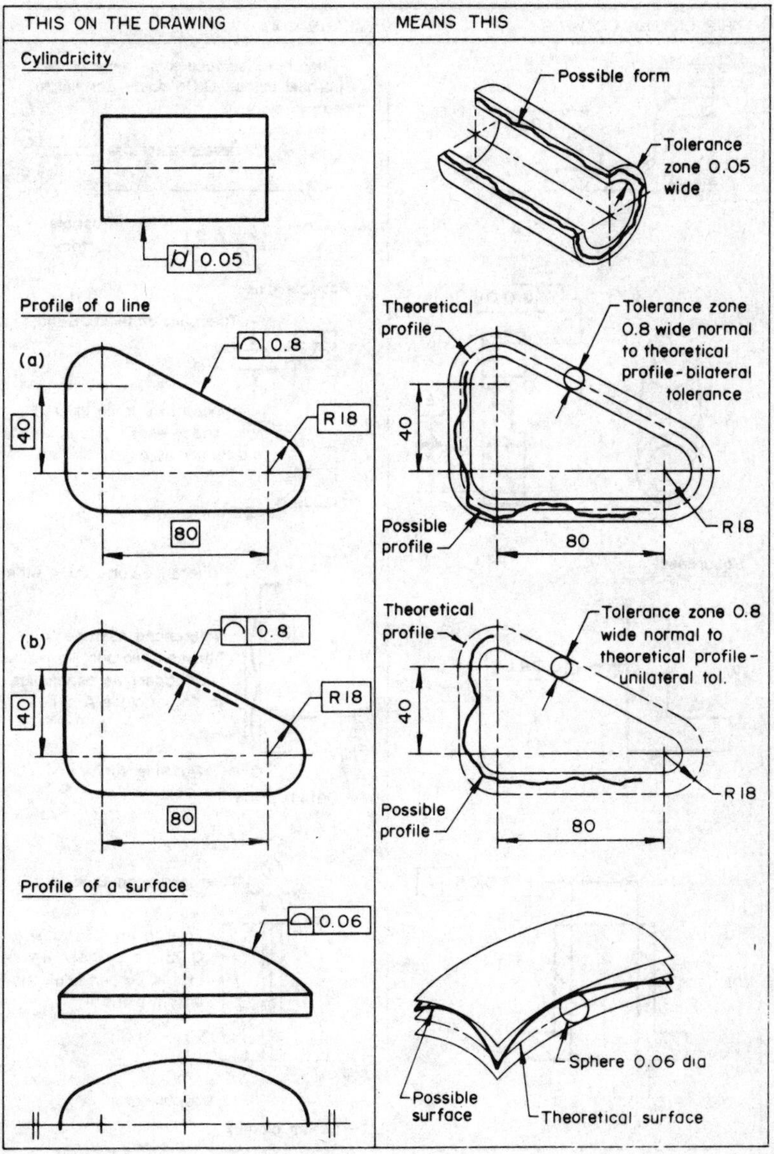

Fig. 3.18 *Examples and Interpretations of Geometrical Tolerances*

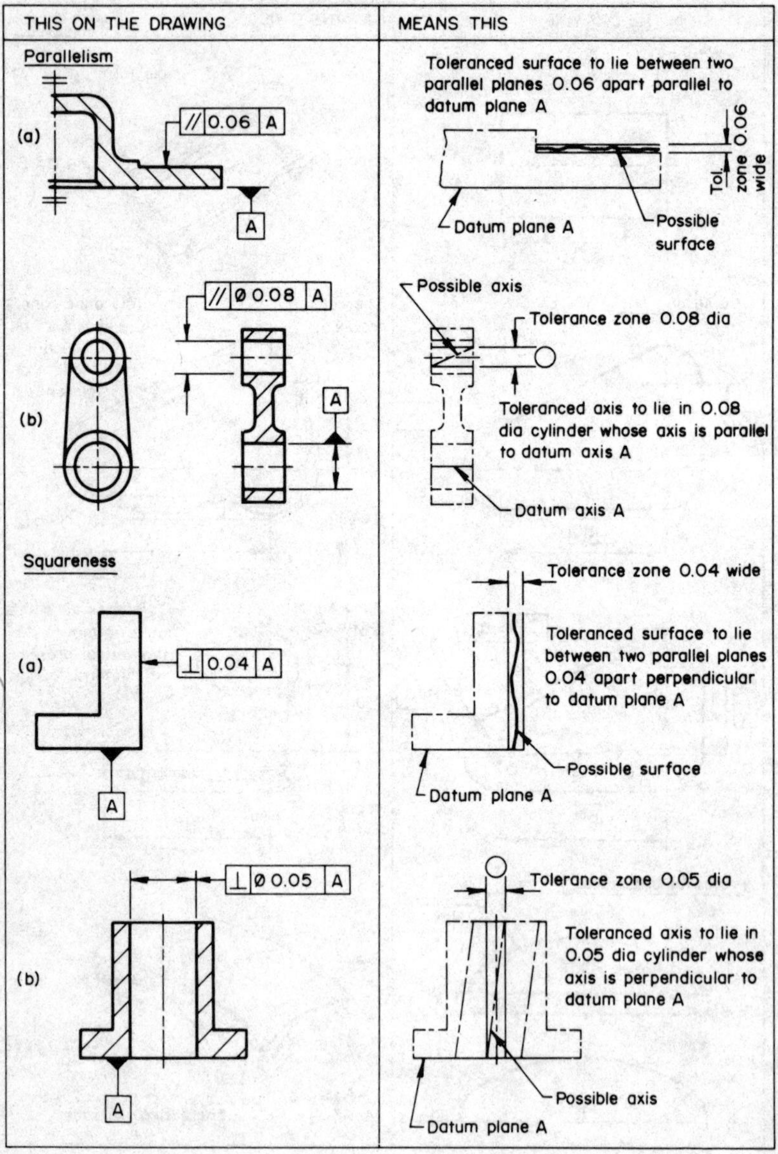

Fig. 3.19 *Examples and Interpretations of Geometrical Tolerances*

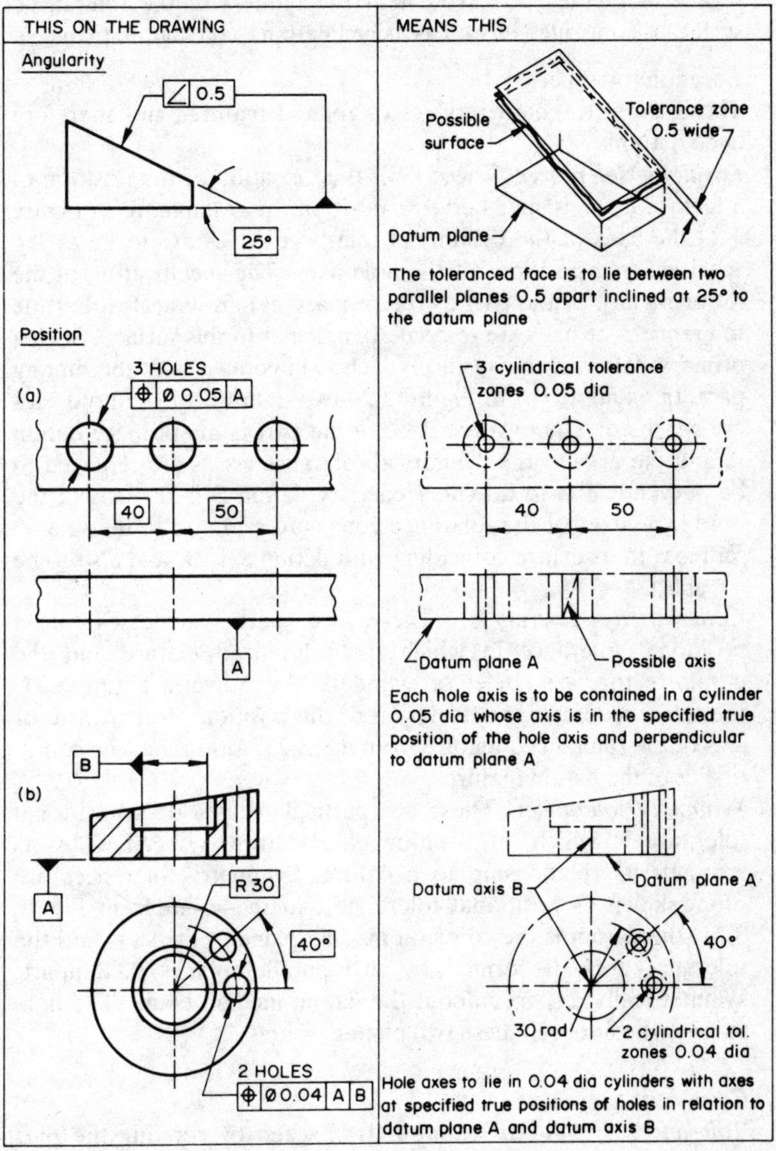

Fig. 3.20 *Examples and Interpretations of Geometrical Tolerances*

Angularity tolerances. An example of an angularity tolerance is shown in Figure 3.20. Note that the flatness of the toleranced surface is controlled as well as its inclination to the datum plane.

Location tolerances

These apply to characteristics of related features and therefore need datums.

Positional tolerances. These limit the deviation of the position of a feature from its specified true position. In example (a) in Figure 3.20 the axes of the cylindrical tolerance zones are to be at the specified true positions of the hole axes. The specification of the lower surface of the part as the primary datum indicates that the tolerance zone axes are to be perpendicular to this surface. Such a primary datum is the surface which is in contact with the mating part. In example (b) in Figure 3.20 two datums for the hole axes are specified. The lower surface of the part is the primary datum A and the axes of the cylindrical tolerance zones are required to be perpendicular to it. The secondary datum B is the axis of the bore. The axes of the tolerance zones are required to lie on a 30 radius with its centre coinciding with datum axis B, and also to be 40° apart.

Concentricity tolerances. These are particular cases of a positional tolerance in which the toleranced feature and the datum feature are circles or cylinders. As shown in Figure 3.21, the tolerance limits the deviation of the position of the centre or axis of the toleranced feature from its true position, i.e. the centre or axis of the datum feature.

Symmetry tolerances. These are particular cases of a positional tolerance in which the position of a feature is specified by its symmetrical relationship to a datum. Symmetry tolerances are often shown as positional tolerances. In the example in Figure 3.21, the datum is the common median plane of the slots and the tolerance zone is formed by two parallel planes 0.08 apart, symmetrically disposed about the datum median plane. The hole axis is to lie between these two planes.

Composite tolerances

Tolerances of run-out. Run-out is checked by rotating the part about a specified datum axis, or by rotating it when supported at two specified datum points. A run-out tolerance may be applied to the surface of a solid of revolution and to the faces of the solid

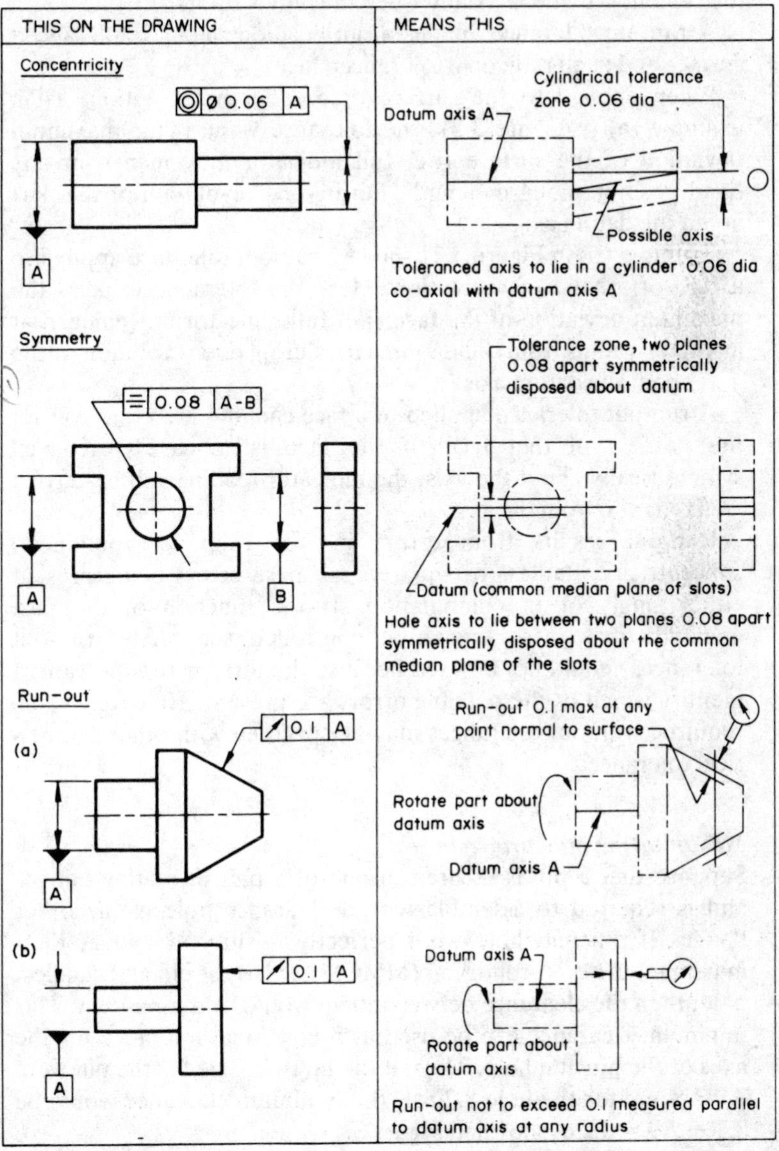

Fig. 3.21 *Examples and Interpretations of Geometrical Tolerances*

perpendicular to the axis. Neither the part or the measuring instrument is to move axially when the part is rotated.

A run-out tolerance applies at all positions along a toleranced surface and at all radii on a toleranced face.

When applied to the surface of a solid of revolution, as in example (a) in Figure 3.21, the tolerance value is the maximum deviation of the surface (i.e. full indicator movement), at any fixed position along its length, during one revolution of the part about the datum axis.

Example (b) in Figure 3.21 shows a run-out tolerance applied to a face of a solid of revolution. Here the tolerance value is the maximum deviation of the face (i.e. full indicator movement), at any fixed radius from the datum axis, during one revolution of the part about the datum axis.

A run-out tolerance applied to a face cannot be used to control the flatness of that face. If the face is concave or convex symmetrically about the axis, the indicator reading will be zero at all fixed radii from the axis.

Run-out results from errors in, for example, roundness, concentricity, flatness or squareness, these errors being present either singly or in combination. If the function of the part demands that these errors be controlled separately, run-out tolerances should not be used because the test for run-out cannot identify which of the possible errors are present. However, when required, run-out tolerances may be specified with other geometrical tolerances.

Maximum material principle

Suppose that a pin is secured in one of a pair of mating flanges and is required to assemble with a clearance hole in the other flange. If pin and hole were perfectly positioned and at their maximum material condition (MMC), i.e. largest pin and smallest hole, then the clearance between them would be a minimum. This minimum clearance can be used as a positional tolerance for the axes of the pin and hole. Thus, if the limits of size for the pin were 7.9/7.8 and for the hole 8.2/8.1, the minimum clearance would be $8.1 - 7.9 = 0.2$ as shown in Figure 3.22(a).

Figure 3.22(b) shows that this clearance can be distributed as positional tolerance between the hole axis and the pin axis, say as 0.1 to each. Note, though, that any distribution can be used,

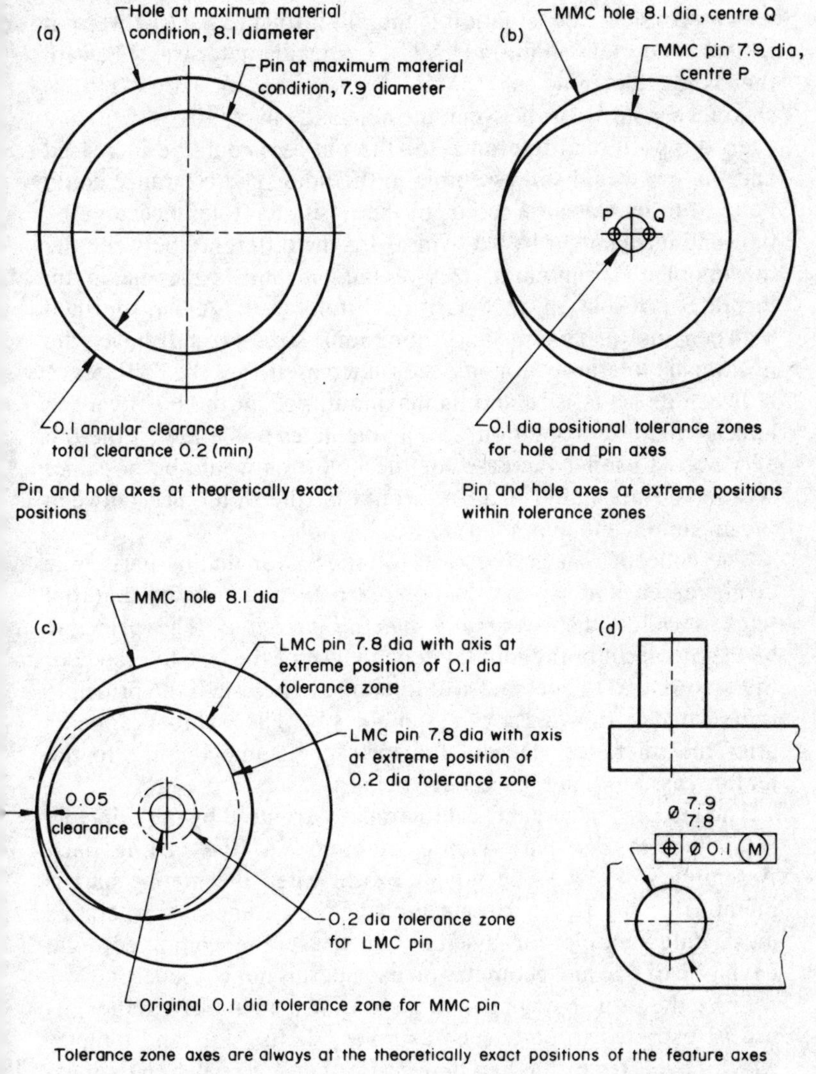
(a)
Hole at maximum material condition, 8.1 diameter
Pin at maximum material condition, 7.9 diameter
0.1 annular clearance total clearance 0.2 (min)
Pin and hole axes at theoretically exact positions
(b)
MMC hole 8.1 dia, centre Q
MMC pin 7.9 dia, centre P
P
Q
0.1 dia positional tolerance zones for hole and pin axes
Pin and hole axes at extreme positions within tolerance zones
(c)
MMC hole 8.1 dia
LMC pin 7.8 dia with axis at extreme position of 0.1 dia tolerance zone
LMC pin 7.8 dia with axis at extreme position of 0.2 dia tolerance zone
0.05 clearance
0.2 dia tolerance zone for LMC pin
Original 0.1 dia tolerance zone for MMC pin
(d)
Ø 7.9 7.8
Ø 0.1 (M)
Tolerance zone axes are always at the theoretically exact positions of the feature axes

Fig. 3.22 *Maximum Material Principle Theory*

provided that the sum of the two positional tolerances does not exceed 0.2. This means that the part which is more difficult to hold for position can be given more of the available tolerance.

Now consider the situation if the pin in Figure 3.22(b) were at its least material condition (LMC), i.e. its diameter was 7.8, with the hole remaining at MMC. Figure 3.22(c) shows that a clearance would exist between the hole and pin of 0.05.

So the positional tolerance for the pin axis could be increased and the pin would still assemble in the hole. The clearance could be used to increase the radius of the positional tolerance zone by 0.05 and its diameter by 0.1. This 0.1 is the difference between the maximum and minimum sizes of the pin and is the maximum increase possible in the positional tolerance. A pin finished between its maximum and minimum sizes would have the positional tolerance for its axis increased by the difference between its actual size and its maximum size. If the hole were in its least material condition, i.e. its diameter was 8.2 with the pin at MMC, a similar increase for the hole axis would be possible. Again, the maximum increase would be the difference between the maximum and minimum sizes of the hole.

The concept that geometrical tolerances for mating parts may be increased if the parts do not reach their maximum material sizes is called the *maximum material principle.* The principle takes into account the mutual dependence of the size tolerance of the feature and the geometrical tolerance. The use of the principle is indicated on drawings by the symbol Ⓜ. The symbol appears after the tolerance value in the tolerance frame relating to the feature, as shown in Figure 3.22(d).

The increase in geometrical tolerance permitted by the principle is applied to one part without reference to the mating part. Assembly will always be possible even when the mating part is manufactured on the extreme limit of the geometrical tolerance most unfavourable for assembly, because the combined total deviation of size and geometry on each part is not exceeded.

Since the principle applies to parts which assemble together, its use is restricted to parts such as holes, shafts, slots and tongues which have axes or median planes. Furthermore, such parts must be subject to geometrical tolerances of straightness, attitude or location. The principle can never be applied to the characteristics of plane surfaces or lines on surfaces.

The use of the maximum material principle results in an increase in manufacturing freedom and a consequent reduction in costs. In addition, it permits the use of fixed (non-adjustable) gauges to check that parts are within the geometrical tolerances. Such gauges simulate the part which is to assemble with the part being checked. However, since the principle permits an increase in geometrical error, the function of the part should be considered to see if the increase is acceptable. For example, the principle should not be used with the positional tolerancing of bores which support gears, since the increase in positional error could lead to incorrect meshing of the gear teeth.

Application of the maximum material principle to datum features
Depending on the functional requirements of a part, the maximum material principle may be applied to datum features as well as to toleranced features. Such applications, if appropriate, will produce a similar increase in manufacturing freedom and reduction in costs, as a result of applying the principle to toleranced features. When the principle is to be applied to datum features the symbol Ⓜ appears after the datum identifying letter or letters in the tolerance frame. There are two general cases and it is important to distinguish clearly between them.

(a) A single toleranced feature is referred to a datum to which the principle is applied.
(b) A group of toleranced features is referred to a datum to which the principle is applied.

Figure 3.23 is an example of the first case. Here the symbol Ⓜ is shown after the tolerance value and the datum identifying letter in the tolerance frame. This means that the diameter of the tolerance zone is allowed to increase from that specified in the tolerance frame as the toleranced feature and datum feature depart from their maximum limits of size. The maximum increase is the sum of the size tolerances on the toleranced feature and the datum feature.

An example of the second case is shown in Figure 3.24. Here a group of two features which is subject to a positional tolerance is referred to a datum feature. The maximum material principle is to be applied to the toleranced features and to the datum, as shown by the symbol Ⓜ appearing after the tolerance value and the datum identifying letter in the tolerance frame.

Departures of the toleranced features from their maximum

Drawing requirement

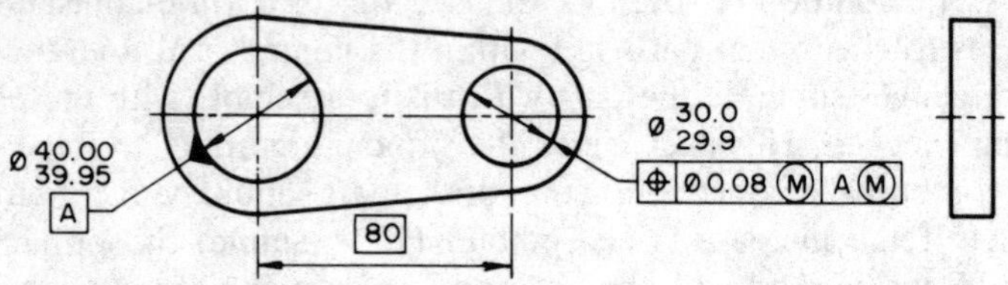

Maximum material principle applied to a single toleranced feature and to the datum feature

Interpretation

(a)

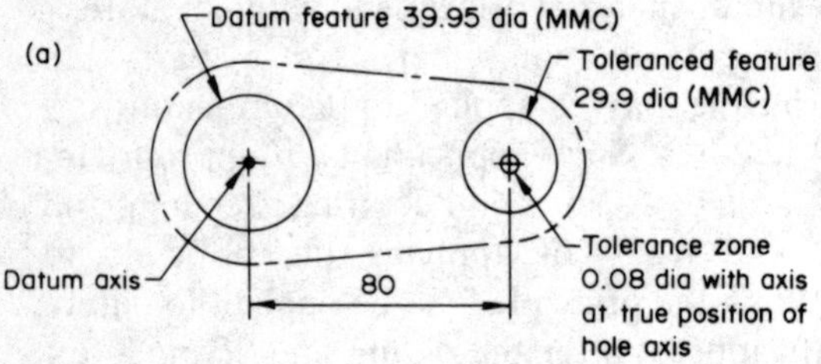

When toleranced feature and datum feature are both at MM tolerance zone diameter is 0.08 as specified in toleranc frame. Toleranced feature axi to be contained in tolerance zor

(b)

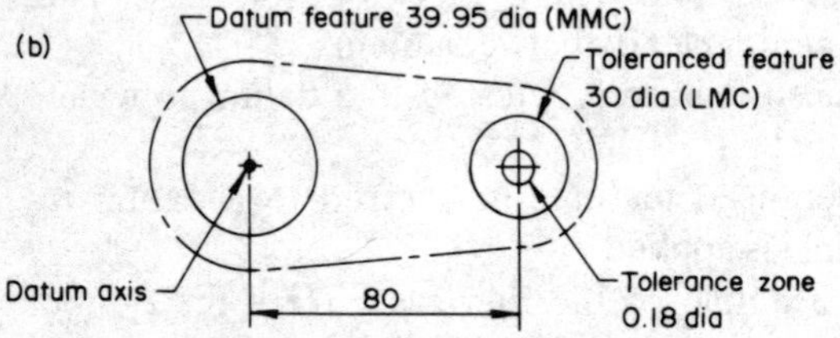

Datum feature at MMC, toleranc feature at LMC. Departure of toleranced feature from MMC 0.1 so tolerance zone diameter is increased to

$$0.08 + 0.1 = 0.18$$

(c)

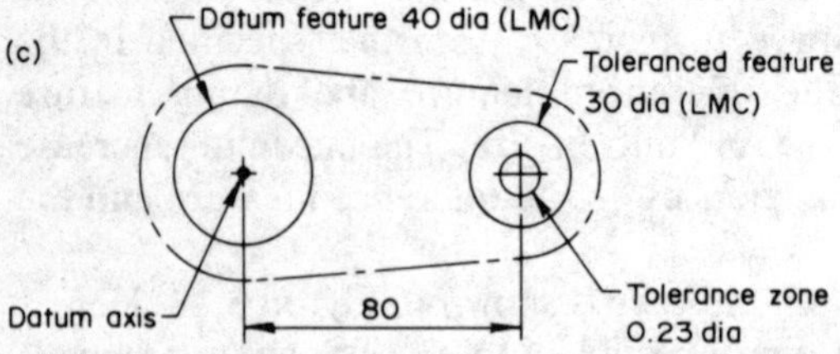

Toleranced feature and datum feature both at LMC. Departure of datum feature from MMC of 0.05 increases tolerance zone diameter to

$$0.08 + 0.1 + 0.05 = 0.23$$

0.23 is maximum diameter of tolerance zone. Actual diameter depends on finished sizes of datur feature and toleranced feature within their limits of size

Fig. 3.23 *Maximum Material Principle Applied to Single Feature and Datum*

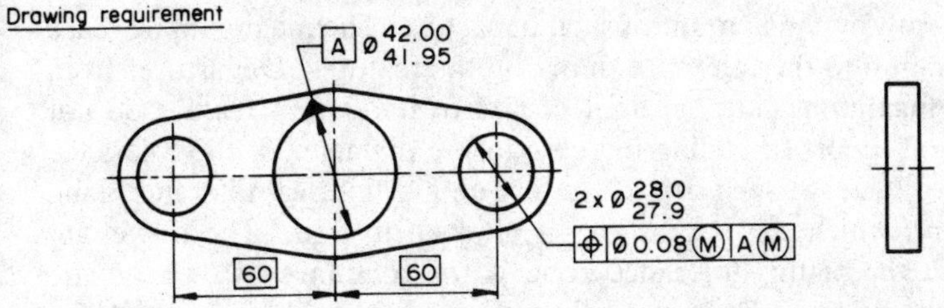

Maximum material principle applied to a group of toleranced features and to the datum feature

Interpretation

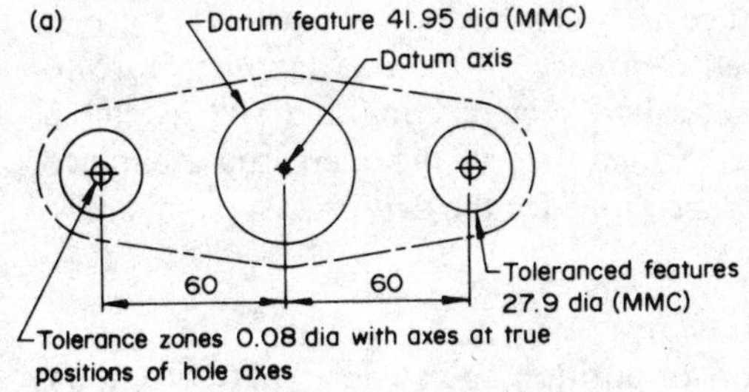

When toleranced feature and datum feature are both at MMC, tolerance zone diameter is 0.08 as specified in tolerance frame. Toleranced feature axes to be contained in tolerance zones

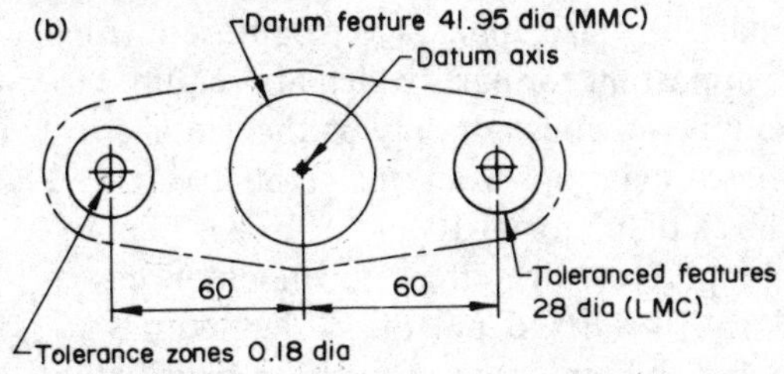

Datum feature at MMC, toleranced features at LMC. Departure of toleranced features from MMC is 0.1 so tolerance zone diameter is increased to

$$0.08 + 0.1 = 0.18$$

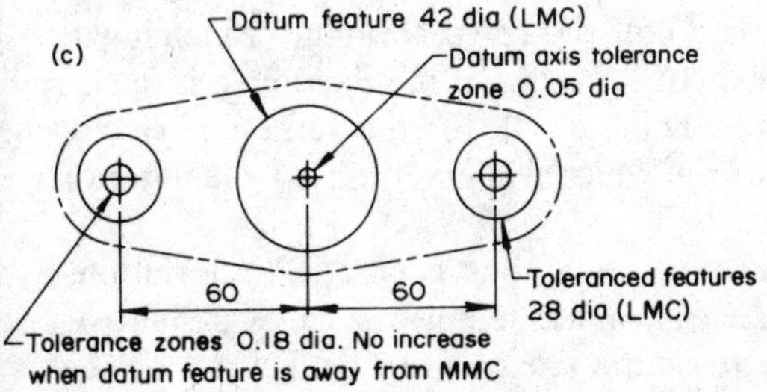

When datum feature is at LMC, the departure of 0.05 from MMC does not increase tolerance zone dia for toleranced features. Instead, datum axis can float in a 0.05 dia tolerance zone the axis of which is in its theoretically exact position relative to the tolerance zone axes for the toleranced features

0.18 is maximum diameter of tolerance zone. Actual diameter depends on finished sizes of toleranced features within their limits of size

Fig. 3.24 *Maximum Material Principle Applied to Group of Features and Datum*

material limit of size permit the diameter of the tolerance zone to increase by the amount of such departure. The maximum increase is limited to the tolerance of 0.1 on the features. Departures from the maximum material limit of size of the datum feature do not permit a corresponding increase in the diameter of the tolerance zone. Instead, such departures create a cylindrical tolerance zone within which the datum axis is allowed to float. The maximum diameter of this tolerance zone is the tolerance of 0.05 on the datum feature. The actual diameter depends on the finished size of the datum feature within its limits of size.

When the datum feature is away from its maximum material limit of size, the clearance between it and its mating feature is increased. This increased clearance allows the datum feature to be away from its theoretically exact position and still assemble with its mating feature. So, in effect, the increased clearance creates a cylindrical tolerance zone for the datum axis.

Virtual condition and virtual size

When a feature has errors of position and some errors of form its size is virtually altered, that is, its size appears to be different from its measured size. This is important for parts which are required to assemble, since free assembly depends not only on the actual sizes of the parts but also on these deviations from true geometry.

For example, if a pin has a diameter of 10 and its axis is bent by 0.1, the smallest hole of perfect form that it will enter has a diameter of 10.1. Similarly, if a fixed pin of 10 diameter is to assemble in a fixed hole and the pin is out of position by 0.1, the smallest perfectly positioned hole of perfect form into which it will assemble has a diameter of 10.1. Again, if the fixed hole is out of square by 0.1 and has a diameter of 10, the largest perfectly positioned pin of perfect form which will enter it has a diameter of 9.9.

From the above it can be seen that geometrical deviations virtually increase the size of a male feature, such as a shaft or tongue, and virtually decrease the size of a female feature such as a hole or slot.

The worst condition for free assembly of a male and female feature occurs when the features are at their MMC sizes, i.e. largest male feature and smallest female feature, and at the same time, the maximum errors allowed by the geometrical tolerances are present. These maximum errors are those permitted when the features are at MMC. The combination of MMC size and maximum geometrical error gives the virtual size of the feature.

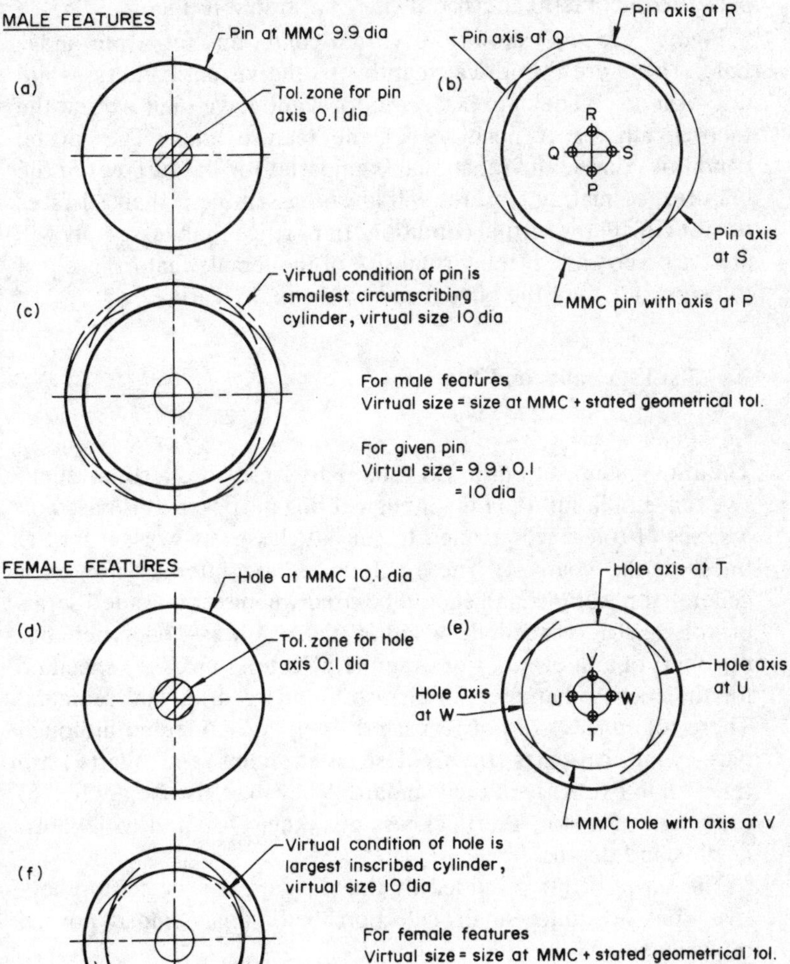

The virtual condition of a feature is perfect in form and at the theoretically exact position of the feature. Mating features will always assemble if the virtual size of the female is equal to or greater than that of the male.

Fig. 3.25 *Virtual Condition and Virtual Size*

For male features the virtual size is the sum of the MMC size and the maximum geometrical error allowed; for female features it is the difference between the MMC size and the maximum permitted geometrical error. This is illustrated in Figure 3.25.

Figure 3.25 also shows the virtual conditions for a pin and a hole. These are cylindrical features so the virtual conditions are also cylinders. They are perfect in form and have their axes at the theoretically exact positions of the feature axes. The virtual conditions define the functional boundaries for the surfaces of the features, so mating features will always assemble if their surfaces do not violate the virtual condition. In practice then, assembly will always be possible if the virtual size of the female feature is equal to or greater than the virtual size of the male feature.

BS 4500 ISO limits and fits

Introduction

The ISO system set out in BS 4500: Part 1 provides a comprehensive range of limits and fits for engineering purposes. It is based on a series of tolerances graded to suit all classes of work from the finest to the coarsest. These tolerances are intended for most general applications and should be used whenever a graded series of tolerances is needed, whether the features concerned are members of a fit or not. For example, ISO tolerances are specified for the cutting diameters of British Standard drills and reamers. These tolerances are not restricted solely to diameters, although only cylindrical parts (briefly designated 'holes' and 'shafts') are referred to explicitly in the standard. They may also be applied to the width of a slot, the thickness of a key, etc., and to lengths, heights and depths.

The range of fits provided by the standard is very comprehensive, but a quite small selection will satisfy most normal requirements.

Definitions

For the purpose of BS 4500 the following definitions apply. They are illustrated in Figure 3.26.

Limits of size. The maximum and minimum sizes permitted for a feature.

Basic size. The size by reference to which the limits of size are

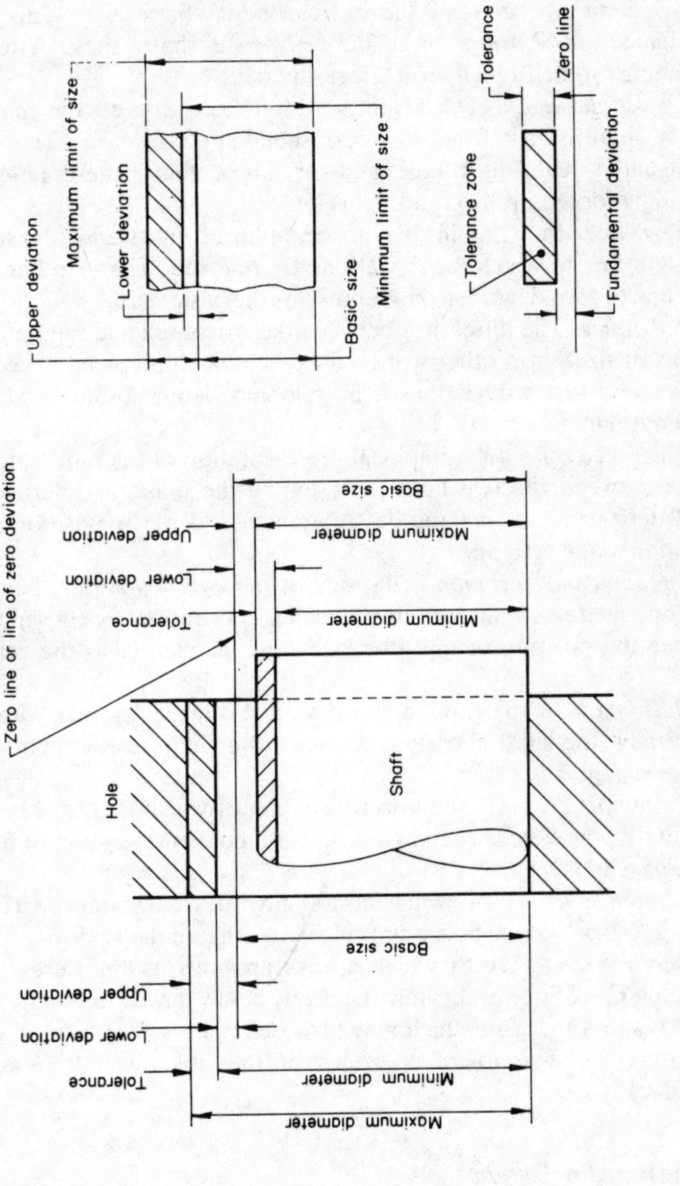

Fig. 3.26 *Terms Used in Limits and Fits*

fixed. The basic size is the same for both members of a fit.

Upper deviation. The algebraic difference between the maximum limit of size and the corresponding basic size. This is designated 'ES' for a hole and 'es' for a shaft, these letters standing for the French term 'écart supérieur'.

Lower deviation. The algebraic difference between the minimum limit of size and the corresponding basic size. This is designated 'EI' for a hole and 'ei' for a shaft, these letters standing for the French term 'écart inférieur'.

Zero line. In a graphical representation of limits and fits, the straight line to which the deviations are referred. The zero line is the line of zero deviation and represents the basic size.

Tolerance. The difference between the maximum and minimum limits of size, or in other words, the algebraic difference between upper and lower deviations. The tolerance is an absolute value without sign.

Tolerance zone. In a graphical representation of tolerances, the zone between the two lines representing the limits of tolerance and defined by its magnitude (tolerance) and by its position in relation to the zero line.

Fundamental deviation. That one of the two deviations, being the one nearest to the zero line, which is conventionally chosen to define the position of the tolerance zone in relation to the zero line.

Basic shaft. A shaft, the upper deviation of which is zero. More generally, the shaft chosen as a basis for a shaft-basis system of fits (see page 61).

Basic hole. A hole, the lower deviation of which is zero. More generally, the hole chosen as a basis for a hole-basis system of fits (see page 61).

Clearance fit. A fit which always provides a clearance. The tolerance zone of the hole is entirely above that of the shaft.

Interference fit. A fit which always provides an interference. The tolerance zone of the hole is entirely below that of the shaft.

Transition fit. A fit which may provide either a clearance or an interference. The tolerance zones of the hole and the shaft overlap.

Limits and fits diagrams

BS 4500 uses a convention for illustrating limits and fits

diagrammatically and this convention is shown in Figure 3.27 for a typical fit. The two rectangles represent the hole and shaft tolerance zones in size, and their positions in relation to the basic size or zero line represent the fundamental deviations. Figure 3.27 illustrates a hole-basis clearance fit (see page 61) but the convention can be used to represent any type of fit.

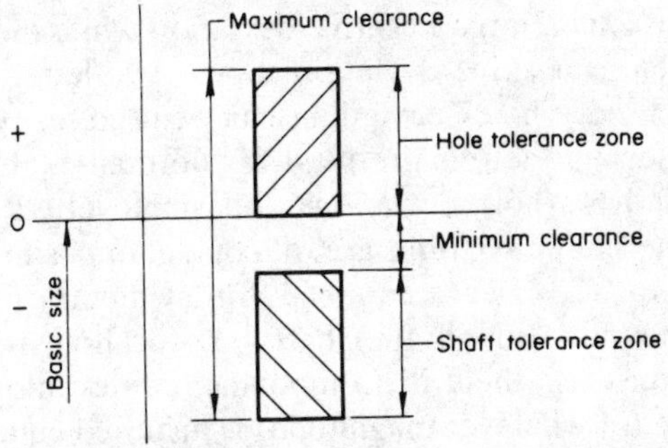

Fig. 3.27 *Fit Represented Conventionally*

Characteristics of the ISO system
To select a fit for a given application, fundamental deviations and tolerances must be selected for both hole and shaft, such that the specified functional requirements are met.

The fundamental deviations position the tolerance zones in relation to the zero line (the basic size). So, they define the maximum material conditions for the members of the fit, i.e. the maximum material limit of size of the shaft and the minimum material limit of size of the hole. The sizes of the tolerances selected depend on the class of work; fine (small) tolerances are needed for fine work and coarse (large) tolerances for coarse work. In combination, the fundamental deviations and tolerances provide fits ranging from loose clearance to heavy interference.

Fundamental deviations
Any fit provided by the system should have the same functional characteristics over a range of sizes. Thus, a precision running fit (close clearance) should provide clearances which give precision running fit conditions at any basic size. A fundamental deviation of fixed size will not do this. Therefore, each fundamental deviation in the system increases at an appropriate rate as the basic size increases.

The system provides 27 fundamental deviations for sizes up to and including 500 mm (and 14 deviations for larger sizes) to give different types of fit ranging from loose clearance to heavy interference.

The total range of sizes covered is subdivided into size ranges and the deviation values for the mean size in each range have been standardized. Each deviation is designated by a letter. The letter 'a' represents a large negative deviation while the letter 'z' represents a large positive deviation. Some two-letter combinations are also used. The 27 deviations can be used for both shafts and holes. The same letters are used for both cases, but capital letters are used for hole deviations and small letters for shaft deviations. The shaft deviations are, of course, opposite in sign to those for holes. To meet the need for symmetrical bilateral tolerances, the deviation j_s for shafts (J_s for holes) has been provided. In this case there is no fundamental deviation and the tolerance zone (of whatever magnitude) is disposed equally about the zero line.

Tolerances

The sizes of the tolerances selected for any fit depend on the quality of fit required. Fine quality fits need fine tolerances while coarse tolerances can be used for coarse fits. As with fundamental deviations, the system provides a range of qualities of tolerances. But, at the same time, a tolerance of a given quality cannot have a fixed size, for a 'fine quality' tolerance on a diameter of say, 200 mm, would not be regarded as 'fine quality' if applied to a 25 mm diameter. So the size of each tolerance quality in the system increases as the basic size increases, at a rate which produces the same quality throughout the size range.

Eighteen tolerance grades are provided, designated IT01, IT0, IT1, IT2, IT3 . . . IT16 (IT stands for ISO series of tolerances). IT01 is the smallest tolerance and IT16 the largest. Grades 14 to 16 do not apply to sizes up to and including 1 mm and grades 01 to 5 do not exist for sizes above 500 mm.

Association of fundamental deviations and tolerances

It was explained above that the nature of a fit is determined by the sizes of the fundamental deviations and tolerances on the hole and shaft. The separate series of fundamental deviations and tolerances can be combined in any way that appears necessary to give a required fit. For example, the deviations H (basic hole) and f (clearance shaft) could be associated, and with each deviation any of the tolerance grades IT01 to IT16 could be used. Since there are 28 different fundamental deviations which apply to both holes and shafts and 18 different tolerance grades, the number of possible combinations is very large. However, many of these combinations may not be of practical use. For example, it is unlikely that combining a very large fundamental deviation (e.g. 'a') with a very small tolerance (e.g. IT01) would serve any practical purpose. In practice, most engineering applications can be met with a restricted selection of fits. On the other hand, the inherent flexibility of the system enables special requirements, outside this restricted range, to be satisfied without difficulty.

Designation of limits and fits

The complete designation of the limits of tolerance for a hole or shaft uses the letter denoting the fundamental deviation followed by the numerical part of the tolerance grade designation.

For example, a hole tolerance with fundamental deviation 'H' and tolerance grade IT7 is designated 'H7'. Similarly, a shaft tolerance with fundamental deviation 'p' and tolerance grade IT6 is designated 'p6'.

The limits of size for a feature are defined by the basic size of the feature, say 45 mm, followed by the tolerance designation, e.g. 45 H7 or 45 p6.

A fit is indicated by combining the basic size common to both features with the designations for each of them. The designation of the hole limits are always given first, e.g. 45 H7–p6 or 45 H7/p6.

Hole-basis and shaft-basis systems of fits

For most general applications the hole-basis system of fits is used. In this system different fits are obtained by combining shafts with varying fundamental deviations with a hole having a fundamental deviation of zero (H). This means, in effect, that the hole is a constant and variations in the shaft give different classes of fit (see Figure 3.28).

The hole-basis system is generally preferred because it is usually easier to manufacture the shaft (by turning and grinding) and measure it than the hole. Thus it is advantageous to be able to allocate the larger part of the tolerance available to the hole and adjust the shaft to suit. Also, if the hole is, in effect, a constant,

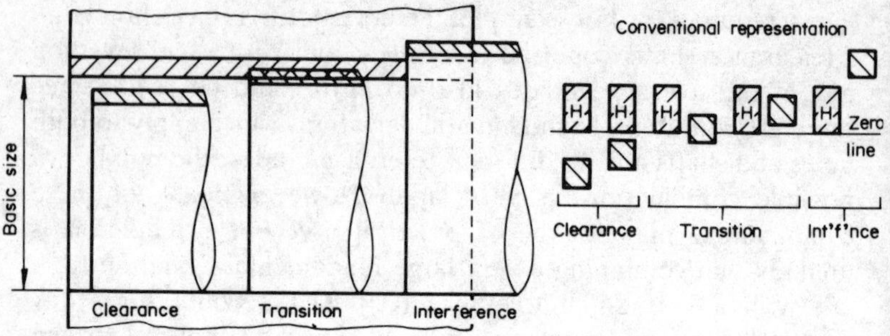

Fig. 3.28 *Hole-based System of Fits*

adjust the shaft to suit. Also, if the hole is, in effect, a constant, the number of drills, reamers and plug gauges used in its manufacture is restricted, which has economic advantages.

There are cases, however, for which it would be preferable to use a shaft-based system of fits. An example is where a single shaft has to carry a variety of items such as bearings, couplings, collars, etc. Here it would be better to keep the shaft constant and vary the bores of the items which are attached to it. This can be done by combining holes with varying fundamental deviations with a shaft having a fundamental deviation of zero (h) (see Figure 3.29). A shaft-based system is particularly appropriate when bar stock is available finished to standard shaft tolerances.

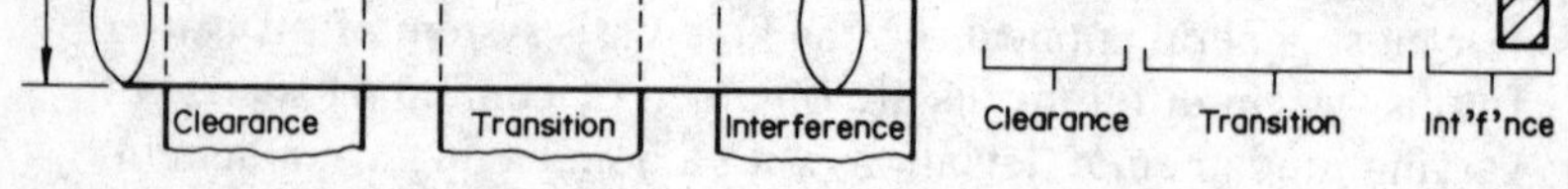

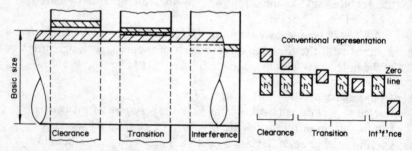

Fig. 3.29 *Shaft-based System of Fits*

Selected fits

As noted earlier, the ISO system, because of its comprehensiveness, will cater for a very wide range of fits. However, the fits required for most engineering products can be provided by a quite limited selection of tolerances and the following are most commonly used.

Selected hole tolerances – H7, H8, H9, H11.
Selected shaft tolerances – c11, d10, e9, f7, g6, h6, k6, n6, p6, s6.

These tolerances are covered by BS 4500A Selected ISO fits – hole basis and BS 4500B Selected ISO fits – shaft basis, and will be found adequate for most applications. Extracts from these latter British Standards are given in Figures 3.30 and 3.31, respectively.

Relationship between basic size and design size

The term *design size* is used in BS 4500 but no definition is given. However, basic size and design size are related as follows. Suppose the designer has determined that a shaft needs to be 50 diameter and it is to run in a bore using an H8/f7 fit. Then the basic size is 50 diameter and is the same for both shaft and hole. The basic size is the theoretical size on which the design size is based.

From Figure 3.30, the limits of tolerance for an H8 hole with a basic size of 50 diameter are 0 and +0.039; for an f7 shaft of the same basic size the limits of tolerance are −0.025 and −0.050.

The design sizes of hole and shaft are those combinations of basic size and limits of tolerance that produce the maximum material hole and maximum material shaft. These design sizes are:

hole, 50 – 0 = 50.000 diameter;
shaft, 50 – 0.025 = 49.975 diameter.

The limits of tolerance associated with these design sizes are:

hole, 0 and +0.039;
shaft, 0 and −0.025.

The limits of size of hole and shaft are the combinations of these limits of tolerance and the design sizes, that is:

hole 50.039 diameter and 50.000 diameter;
shaft 49.975 diameter and 49.950 diameter.

Example of the application of BS 4500

Figure 3.32(a) shows a tongue and lever arrangement as it appears on the design scheme. Dimensions are required for the details to achieve the fits for the shaft in the bore and the pin in its mating hole, and to achieve the two specified clearances.

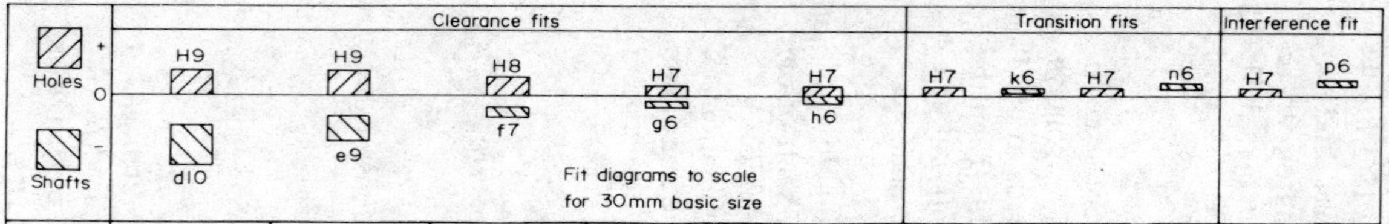

Nom size		Tolerance		Tolerance		Tolerance		Tolerance		Tolerance		Tolerance		Tolerance		Tolerance	
Over	To	H9	d10	H9	e9	H8	f7	H7	g6	H7	h6	H7	k6	H7	n6	H7	p6
mm	mm	0.001mm		0.001mm		0.001mm		0.001mm		0.001mm		0.001mm		0.001mm		0.001mm	
—	3	+25 0	-20 -60	+25 0	-14 -39	+14 0	-6 -16	+10 0	-2 -8	+10 0	-6 0	+10 0	+6 0	+10 0	+10 +4	+10 0	+12 +6
3	6	+30 0	-30 -78	+30 0	-20 -50	+18 0	-10 -22	+12 0	-4 -12	+12 0	-8 0	+12 0	+9 +1	+12 0	+16 +8	+12 0	+20 +12
6	10	+36 0	-40 -98	+36 0	-25 -61	+22 0	-13 -28	+15 0	-5 -14	+15 0	-9 0	+15 0	+10 +1	+15 0	+19 +10	+15 0	+24 +15
10	18	+43 0	-50 -120	+43 0	-32 -75	+27 0	-16 -34	+18 0	-6 -17	+18 0	-11 0	+18 0	+12 +1	+18 0	+23 +12	+18 0	+29 +18
18	30	+52 0	-65 -149	+52 0	-40 -92	+33 0	-20 -41	+21 0	-7 -20	+21 0	-13 0	+21 0	+15 +2	+21 0	+28 +15	+21 0	+35 +22
30	50	+62 0	-80 -180	+62 0	-50 -112	+39 0	-25 -50	+25 0	-9 -25	+25 0	-16 0	+25 0	+18 +2	+25 0	+33 +17	+25 0	+42 +26
50	80	+74 0	-100 -220	+74 0	-60 -134	+46 0	-30 -60	+30 0	-10 -29	+30 0	-19 0	+30 0	+21 +2	+30 0	+39 +20	+30 0	+51 +32
80	120	+87 0	-120 -260	+87 0	-72 -159	+54 0	-36 -71	+35 0	-12 -34	+35 0	-22 0	+35 0	+25 +3	+35 0	+45 +23	+35 0	+59 +37
120	180	+100 0	-145 -305	+100 0	-84 -185	+63 0	-43 -83	+40 0	-14 -39	+40 0	-25 0	+40 0	+28 +3	+40 0	+52 +27	+40 0	+68 +43
180	250	+115 0	-170 -355	+115 0	-100 -215	+72 0	-50 -96	+46 0	-15 -44	+46 0	-29 0	+46 0	+33 +4	+46 0	+60 +31	+46 0	+79 +50
250	315	+130 0	-190 -400	+130 0	-110 -240	+81 0	-56 -108	+52 0	-17 -49	+52 0	-32 0	+52 0	+36 +4	+52 0	+66 +34	+52 0	+88 +56
315	400	+140 0	-210 -440	+140 0	-125 -265	+89 0	-62 -119	+57 0	-18 -54	+57 0	-36 0	+57 0	+40 +4	+57 0	+73 +37	+57 0	+98 +62

Complete table covers nominal sizes to 500mm and includes H11 - c11 and H7 - s6 fits

Fig. 3.30 *Selected ISO Hole-basis Fits from BS 4500A*

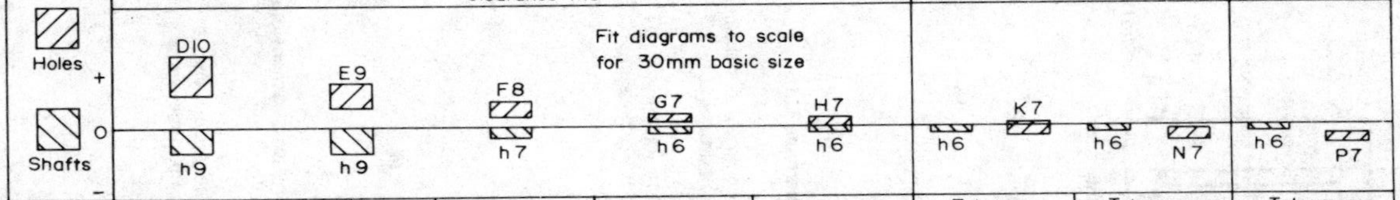

Nom size		Clearance fits										Transition fits				Interference fit	
		Tolerance		Tolerance		Tolerance		Tolerance		Tolerance		Tolerance		Tolerance		Tolerance	
Over	To	h9	D10	h9	E9	h7	F8	h6	G7	h6	H7	h6	K7	h6	N7	h6	P7
mm	mm	0.001mm		0.001mm		0.001mm		0.001mm		0.001mm		0.001mm		0.001mm		0.001mm	
—	3	0 -25	+60 +20	0 -25	+39 +14	0 -10	+20 +6	0 -6	+12 +2	0 -6	+10 0	0 -6	0 -10	0 -6	-4 -14	0 -6	-6 -16
3	6	0 -30	+78 +30	0 -30	+50 +20	0 -12	+28 +10	0 -8	+16 +4	0 -8	+12 0	0 -8	+3 -9	0 -8	-4 -16	0 -8	-8 -20
6	10	0 -36	+98 +40	0 -36	+61 +25	0 -15	+35 +13	0 -9	+20 +5	0 -9	+15 0	0 -9	+5 -10	0 -9	-4 -19	0 -9	-9 -24
10	18	0 -43	+120 +50	0 -43	+75 +32	0 -18	+43 +16	0 -11	+24 +6	0 -11	+18 0	0 -11	+6 -12	0 -11	-5 -23	0 -11	-11 -29
18	30	0 -52	+149 +65	0 -52	+92 +40	0 -21	+53 +20	0 -13	+28 +7	0 -13	+21 0	0 -13	+6 -15	0 -13	-7 -28	0 -13	-14 -35
30	50	0 -62	+180 +80	0 -62	+112 +50	0 -25	+64 +25	0 -16	+34 +9	0 -16	+25 0	0 -16	+7 -18	0 -16	-8 -33	0 -16	-17 -42
50	80	0 -74	+220 +100	0 -74	+134 +60	0 -30	+76 +30	0 -19	+40 +10	0 -19	+30 0	0 -19	+9 -21	0 -19	-9 -39	0 -19	-21 -51
80	120	0 -87	+260 +120	0 -87	+159 +72	0 -35	+90 +36	0 -22	+47 +12	0 -22	+35 0	0 -22	+10 -25	0 -22	-10 -45	0 -22	-24 -59
120	180	0 -100	+305 +145	0 -100	+185 +85	0 -40	+106 +43	0 -25	+54 +14	0 -25	+40 0	0 -25	+12 -28	0 -25	-12 -52	0 -25	-28 -68
180	250	0 -115	+355 +170	0 -115	+215 +100	0 -46	+122 +50	0 -29	+61 +15	0 -29	+46 0	0 -29	+13 -33	0 -29	-14 -60	0 -29	-33 -79
250	315	0 -130	+400 +190	0 -130	+240 +110	0 -52	+137 +56	0 -32	+69 +17	0 -32	+52 0	0 -32	+16 -36	0 -32	-14 -66	0 -32	-36 -88
315	400	0 -140	+440 +210	0 -140	+265 +125	0 -57	+151 +62	0 -36	+75 +18	0 -36	+57 0	0 -36	+17 -40	0 -36	-16 -73	0 -36	-41 -98

Complete table covers nominal sizes to 500mm and includes h11-C11 and h6-S7 fits

Fig. 3.31 *Selected ISO Shaft-basis Fits from BS 4500B*

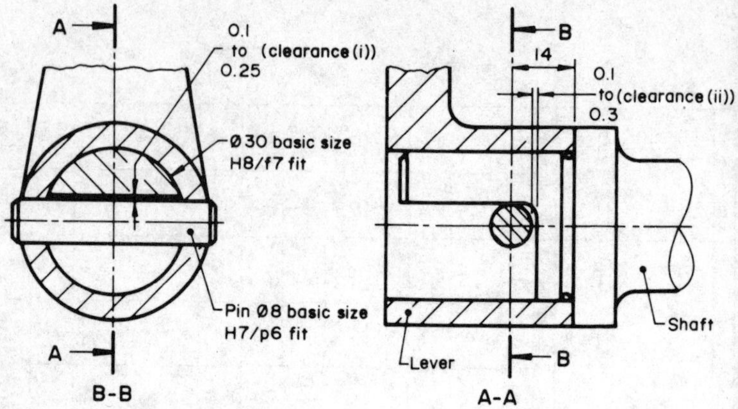

(a) Extract from design scheme

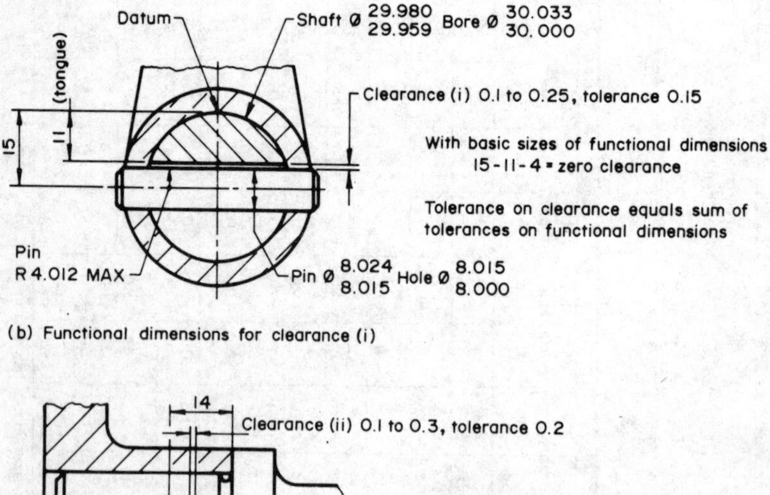

(b) Functional dimensions for clearance (i)

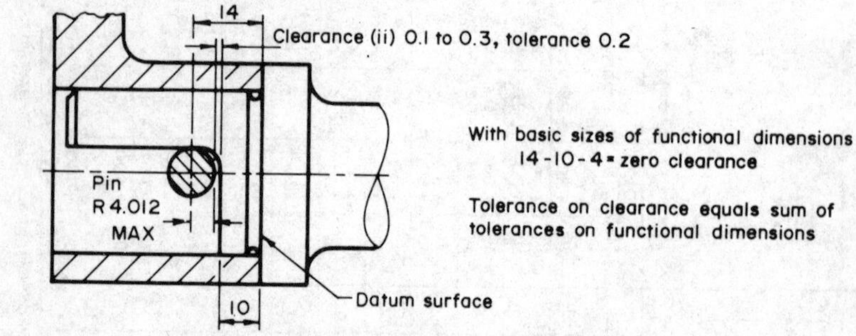

(c) Functional dimensions for clearance (ii)

Fig. 3.32 *Dimensions for Tongued Shaft and Lever*

Calculation of fits

Consider first the two fits. From the extract from BS 4500A in Figure 3.30 the limits of tolerance for an H8/f7 fit on a basic size of 30 diameter are given as 0 and +0.033 for the hole and −0.020 and −0.041 for the shaft. So the limits of size are:

hole, 30.033/30.000 diameter;
shaft, 29.980/29.959 diameter.

Also, from BS 4500A, the limits of tolerance for an H7/p6 fit for a basic size of 8 diameter are given as 0 and +0.015 for the hole and +0.024 and +0.015 for the shaft. So the limits of size are:

hole 8.015/8.000 diameter;
shaft 8.024/8.015 diameter.

Calculation of clearances (i)

Now consider clearance (i) between the side of the tongue and the pin, specified on the scheme to be between 0.1 and 0.25. From Figure 3.32(b) it can be seen that if this clearance were zero the basic sizes would be 11 for the thickness of the tongue, 15 from the side of the 30 diameter bore to the pin axis and 4 for the radius of the pin. These are the functional dimensions which affect clearance (i) and so:

$$15 - 11 - 4 = \text{zero clearance}$$

For the clearance to be its specified minimum of 0.1 the pin diameter must be at its maximum of 8.024 diameter, or 4.012 radius. The dimension equation above then becomes:

$$0.1 = 15 - 11 - 4.012 + 0.112$$

The 0.112 figure is necessary to balance the equation. It can be eliminated by adding 0.112 to the 15 dimension or subtracting 0.112 from the 11 dimension. If we choose the second option the dimension equation reduces to:

$$0.1 = 15 - 10.888 - 4.012$$

These values are the design sizes of the functional dimensions and it is necessary to allocate tolerances to them.

The sum of the tolerances on the design sizes must equal the tolerance on the clearance which is 0.25 − 0.1 = 0.15. The tolerance on the pin diameter is already fixed at 0.009, i.e. 8.024 − 8.015, so the tolerance on the pin radius is 0.0045. This can be rounded to 0.004. So the sum of the tolerances on the other two dimensions is 0.15 − 0.004 = 0.146. We might choose to allocate 0.088 of this to the 10.888 dimension, leaving 0.058 for the 15 dimension. The general rule is to give more of the available tolerance to the dimensions that are difficult to control. We can now write a tolerance equation as:

$$0.15 = 0.058 + 0.088 + 0.004$$

Now we have to decide the limits of tolerance for the functional dimensions. This is done by combining the dimension equation and the tolerance equation to form a limits-of-tolerance equation. This takes account of the signs of the functional dimensions. Since the clearance is positive (+0.1) and has a positive limit of tolerance (+0.15), positive dimensions have positive limits of tolerance and vice versa. So the limits-of-tolerance equation becomes:

$$0.1\,^{+0.15}_{\;0} = 15\,^{+0.058}_{\;0} - 10.888\,^{\;0}_{-0.088} - 4.012\,^{\;0}_{-0.004}$$

Expressed as limits of size the functional dimensions are:

15.058/15.000, 10.888/10.800, with a pin diameter of 8.024/8.015

Check calculation. As a check, use the calculated values of the functional dimensions to work out the maximum and minimum clearances. The maximum clearance occurs when the pin radius is a minimum, the tongue thickness is a minimum and the distance to the pin axis is a maximum.

Therefore:

$$\text{maximum clearance} = 15.058 - 10.800 - 4.008 = 0.25$$
$$\text{minimum clearance} = 15.000 - 10.888 - 4.012 = 0.1$$

These are the specified maximum and minimum values of the clearance so the functional dimensions are satisfactory.

The procedure outlined above is explained in more detail in the BSI publication PP 7309 An introduction to the tolerancing of functional length dimensions.

Calculation of clearance (ii)
The same procedure can be used to determine the functional dimensions and their tolerances to achieve clearance (ii). From Figure 3.32(c) we see that given the scheme dimension of 14 which locates the pin axis, and a basic diameter of 8 for the pin, a basic dimension of 10 is required on the shaft from the datum surface to the end of the tongue. If clearance (ii) were zero then the dimension equation in terms of basic sizes can be written as:

$$14 - 10 - 4 \text{ (pin radius)} = \text{zero clearance}$$

For a minimum clearance of 0.1, the pin radius must be a maximum of 4.012, so

$$0.1 = 14 - 10 - 4.012 + 0.112$$

Eliminating the balancing figure of 0.112 by adding it to the 14 basic dimension, we have a dimension equation in design sizes of:

$$0.1 = 14.112 - 10 - 4.012$$

The tolerance on the clearance is 0.2 which must equal the sum of the tolerances on the functional dimensions. The tolerance on the pin radius is 0.0045 which can be rounded to 0.004. So a possible tolerance equation is:

$$0.2 = 0.088 + 0.108 + 0.004$$

Combining this with the dimension equation to form a limits-of-tolerance equation gives:

$$0.1\,^{+0.2}_{\;\;0} = 14.112\,^{+0.088}_{\;\;0} - 10\,^{\;\;0}_{-0.108} - 4.012\,^{\;\;0}_{-0.004}$$

From this the limits of size of the functional dimensions are:
14.200/14.112, 10.000/9.892 with a pin diameter of 8.024/8.015

Check calculation. Writing check equations for the maximum and minimum clearances gives:

$$\text{maximum clearance} = 14.200 - 9.892 - 4.008 = 0.3$$
$$\text{minimum clearance} = 14.112 - 10.000 - 4.012 = 0.1$$

These are the specified limits for the clearance so the functional dimensions are satisfactory.

4 Surface texture

As noted in chapter 3, all manufactured parts depart from absolute perfection to some degree. The sizes of individual features on similar parts will vary, leading to the use of size tolerances, and the features will have deviations from true geometry, which may need to be controlled by geometrical tolerances. By the same token no manufactured surface will be perfectly smooth but will exhibit imperfections of various sorts. Controlling these by specifying a suitable quality of finish, or *surface texture*, can lead to longer component life, cost-efficient manufacture and functional interchangeability. The assessment of surface texture is covered in the two parts of BS 1134. These deal in detail with method and instrumentation, and give general information and guidance.

The control of surface texture

In general, surface-texture control does not seek superlative finishes on components, but it attempts to secure, at the lowest cost, a surface texture which experience has shown will enable the part to function satisfactorily. The control of surface texture can be approached in two ways. The first specifies the requirements for all surfaces, on the grounds that each has an essential surface pattern and degree of roughness determined by functional or economic reasons. With this approach the functional benefits of surface-texture control are secured, but only those surfaces for which higher finishing costs are justified will be controlled closely. With the second approach, control is only applied to those surfaces where it is functionally essential, leaving the remainder to normal good machining and finishing practice, provided that the specified dimensional accuracy of the features is obtained. This good practice could of course vary from one machine shop to another.

Whichever approach is used, the coarsest surface texture compatible with satisfactory functioning should be specified to keep finishing costs to a minimum. Thus, a very fine surface texture would be required for the surface of a shaft for a hydraulic cylinder reciprocating through and sealed by an 'O' ring, whereas a relatively coarse, oil retaining texture would be specified for a machine slideway.

Geometry of surfaces

Machined surfaces are produced by three general types of tool: *single-point tools*, such as those used on lathes, shapers and planers; *single-line tools*, such as milling cutters; and *'multi-point' tools*, such as grinding wheels and linishing belts.

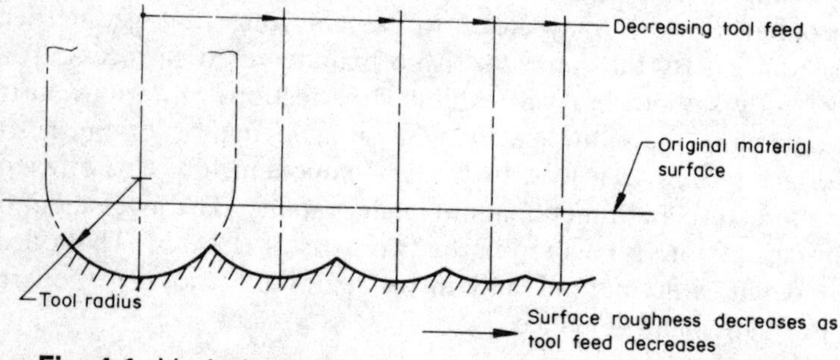

Fig. 4.1 *Variation of Surface Roughness with Tool Feed*

Single-point and single-line tools make successive overlapping cuts which form a series of peaks and valleys. The height and spacing of these vary with the feed of the tool. The finer the feed, the smaller the peaks and valleys and the closer their spacing, hence the smoother the surface, as shown in Figure 4.1. Multi-point cutting, using a grinding wheel for example, produces a series of gashes on the cut surface.

The texture or *surface roughness* of a machined surface is characteristic of the process which produced it, and may be detected by appearance or feel. Besides departures from true geometric form there is also a *waviness* present on the surface which is brought about by vibration and machine deflection. In addition, the direction of the predominant surface pattern, called *lay*, can be seen on most machined surfaces. Lay is determined by the production process. Roughness, waviness, and lay are illustrated in Figure 4.2.

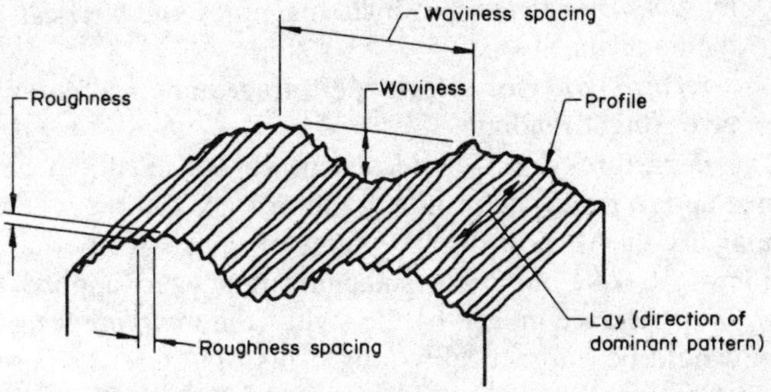

Fig. 4.2 *Surface Characteristics*

The measurement of surface texture

A full description of the measurement of surface texture is outside the scope of this book and the interested reader should consult BS 1134: Part 1. Only the essentials are dealt with here.

An ideally complete assessment of surface texture would require the measurement of all departures from the ideal surface, together with an assessment of the effect of the combined texture on the functioning of the surface. The problems involved in making such a complete assessment are overcome by confining measurements to profiles of plane sections taken through the surface, that is, by taking single-line traces.

Most surface-texture measurement is done using a stylus instrument. This has the following main parts, illustrated diagrammatically in Figure 4.3:

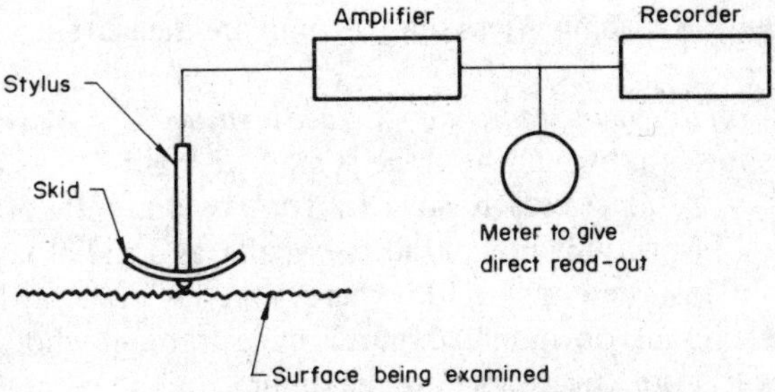

Fig. 4.3 *Stylus Instrument*

(a) a *skid* which, when drawn over the surface, provides a datum;

(b) a *stylus*;

(c) an *amplifying device* which magnifies the vertical movements of the stylus;

(d) a *recording device* to provide a trace and/or a meter which gives direct readings.

The departures from an ideal surface are small, in absolute terms, and to make the profile graph or trace clear it is necessary to magnify the vertical displacements of the stylus, perhaps by a factor of 10 000, but if this magnification were applied to the horizontal distance moved by the stylus (the *sampling length*), the trace would be impracticably long. This would be the case even for the commonly used sampling length of 0.8 mm. Therefore, the vertical and horizontal magnifications are chosen independently.

It can be seen from Figure 4.2 that a short sampling length taken, say, at the top of a wave, will provide a measure of the roughness while suppressing waviness and form errors. This roughness measure will be nominally the same for all parts of the surface but may vary considerably from point to point. These variations can be overcome by taking the mean of a number of observations.

The observations may be conveniently taken in a row along a short length of the surface. So, if the roughness is less than some given sampling length, say 0.8 mm, the trace is divided into successive sections each 0.8 mm long and the average height of each section is found. Taking a mean value from about five consecutive sections will eliminate the effects of variations between successive sections. Thus, the more widely spaced components of the texture are eliminated from the profile and only those whose spacing is less than 0.8 mm are measured.

Effect of lay on the measurement of surface texture

Figure 4.2 shows that when the trace is made at right angles to the lay the peaks are most closely spaced. The lay is usually obvious from a visual inspection. For parallel, circular and radial lays the direction of measurement should be across the lay. Where the lay is multi-directional or indeterminate, measurement should be made in several directions and the maximum roughness accepted as the value for the surface. Crossed lay should be traced at 45° to average the effects of the two directions.

Numerical expression of roughness

The roughness of a surface can be expressed in a number of ways, but the most commonly used is the *roughness average* R_a. This was previously known as the *centre-line-average* (CLA) and is described in BS 1134: Part 1 as the *arithmetical mean deviation*. It is defined as the arithmetical average value of the departure of the profile above and below the reference line throughout the prescribed sampling length and is measured in micrometres (μm), i.e. 0.001 mm. Modern stylus instruments give direct read-outs making the determination of roughness values from traces unnecessary.

The preferred values of R_a in micrometres are as follows:
50 (very rough), 25, 12.5, 6.3, 3.2, 1.6, 0.8, 0.4, 0.2, 0.1, 0.05, 0.025 and 0.0125 (very fine).

Roughness comparison specimens

These are electro-formed sample blocks covering the preferred range of surface texture values whose surfaces have a known roughness average R_a, simulating various production processes. They are used to give designers guidance on the feel and appearance of surfaces produced by a process and its surface texture value. They also assist workshop personnel to evaluate and control workpiece surfaces by visual and tactile comparison with the specimen surface. An often used tactile method is to run a finger nail along the surfaces of the comparator block and the machined part. Roughness comparison specimens are dealt with in BS 2634.

Indication of surface texture on drawings

BS 308: Part 2 gives the symbols used to indicate surface texture and machining requirements on drawings. Surface-texture values can be added to the symbols as required.

Symbols indicating surface texture

The basic symbol, shown in Figure 4.4(a), is a tick, the legs of which are of unequal length inclined at about 60° to the line representing the surface. If material is to be removed by machining, a bar is added to the basic symbol, as in Figure 4.4(b).

If removal of material is not permitted, a circle is added to the basic symbol, as in Figure 4.4(c). This symbol is also used to indicate that a surface is to be left in the state produced by a

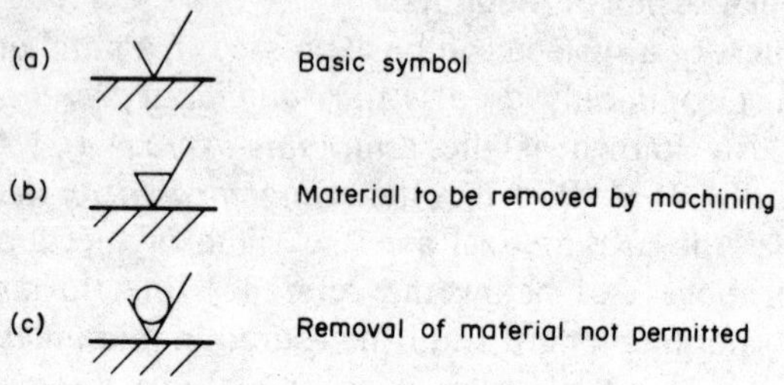

Fig. 4.4 *Surface Texture Symbols*

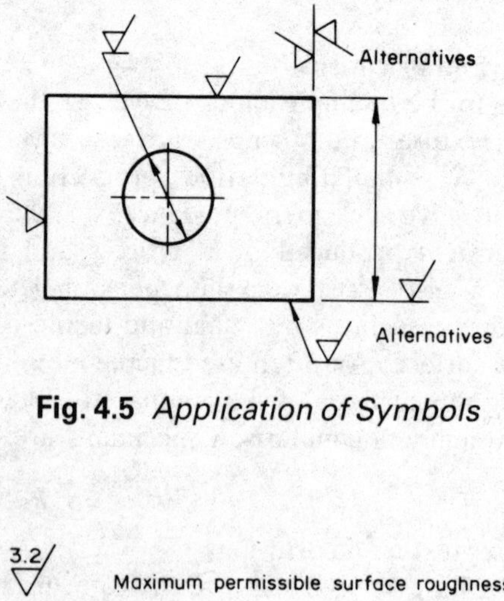

Fig. 4.5 *Application of Symbols*

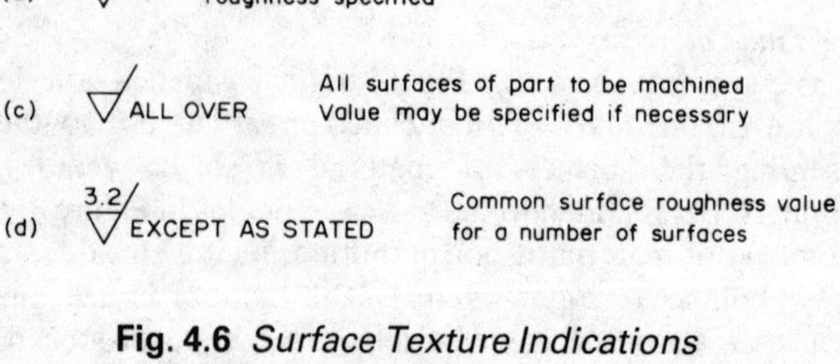

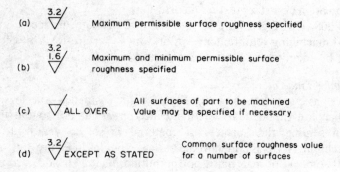

Fig. 4.6 *Surface Texture Indications*

preceding manufacturing process, whether that state was achieved by removal of material or not.

The line thickness of the symbols should be the same as that used for the dimensions on the drawing.

Application of the symbols

In general, machining and surface-texture symbols should be shown once only on each surface, preferably on the same view as the size or location dimensions of the surface. The symbol should be normal to the line on which it is placed, as shown in Figure 4.5.

Values added to the symbols should be arranged so that they can be read from the bottom or right-hand side of the drawing.

Indications added to the symbols

Allowable surface texture

The R_a value or values are added to the symbols as illustrated in Figure 4.6. When only one value is shown, as in Figure 4.6(a), it represents the maximum permissible roughness. If two values are shown, as in Figure 4.6(b), the upper gives the maximum permissible surface roughness and the lower the minimum. Where all surfaces of the part are to be machined, a general note as shown in Figure 4.6(c) may be used. If necessary, a value may be added to the symbol. Where the same surface-texture value applies to a number of surfaces, the symbol and value may be omitted from the surfaces and given instead in a general note, as in Figure 4.6(d).

Additional special requirements

Figure 4.7(a) shows how additional special requirements concerned with surface texture may be added around the symbol and examples are shown in Figure 4.7(b–d). In Figure 4.7(b) a sampling length other than the commonly used 0.8 mm is specified and in Figure 4.7(c) the method by which the surface is to be produced is specified. In Figure 4.7(d) the surface is to be finally finished by chromium plating, the extent of the plating being indicated by the thick chain line. The figure also shows how roughness values before and after plating are applied to the surface.

Where control of lay direction is necessary the symbols in Figure 4.8 are used, placed in position 'd' in Figure 4.7(a). An

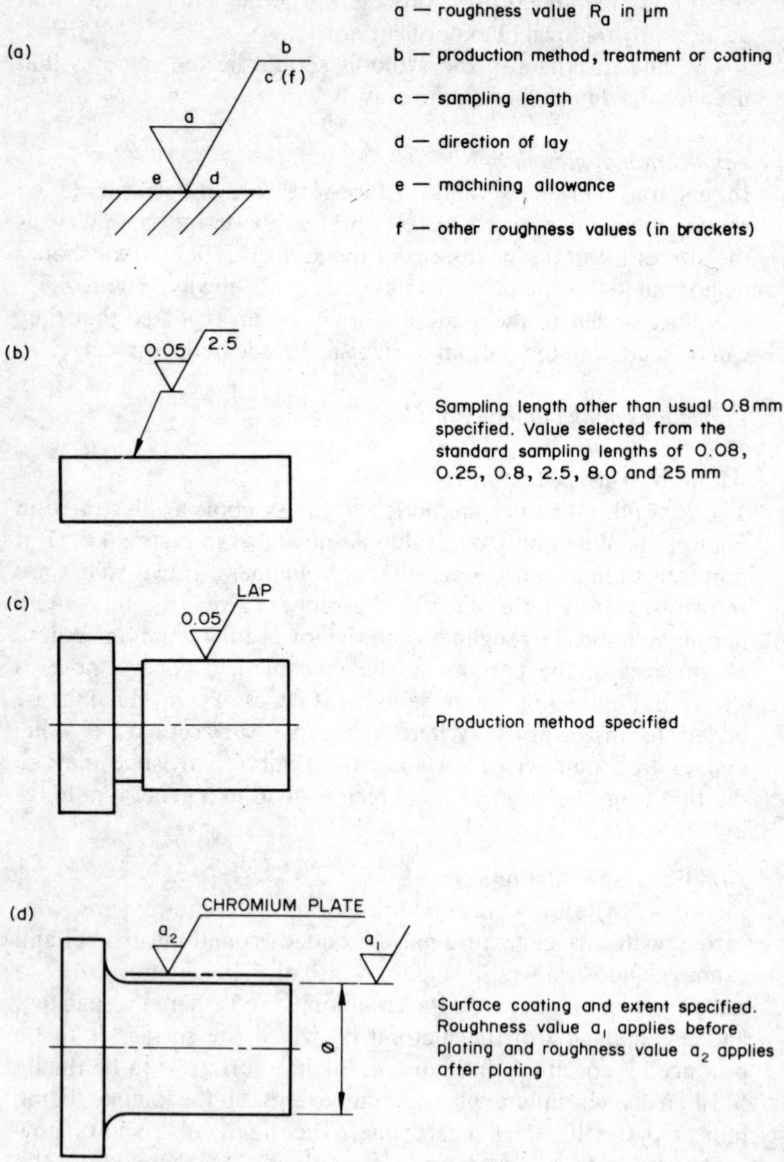

Fig. 4.7 *Specifying Additional Requirements*

Symbols for the direction of lay		
Symbol	**Example of use**	**Interpretation**
=	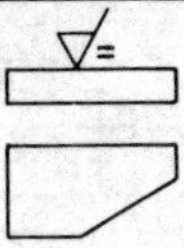	Parallel to the plane of projection of the view in which the symbol is used 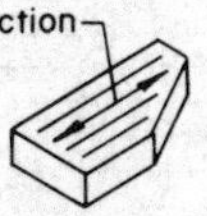
⊥	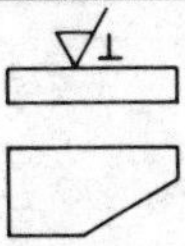	Perpendicular to the plane of projection of the view in which the symbol is used 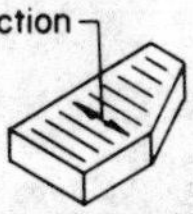
X	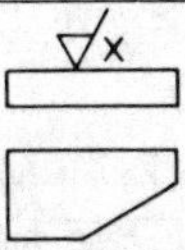	Crossed in two slant directions relative to the plane of projection of the view in which the symbol is used 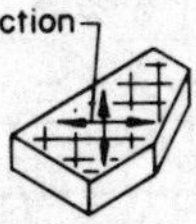
M	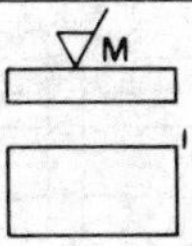	Multi-directional 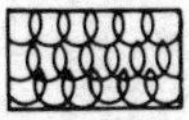
C	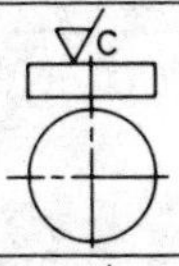	Approximately circular relative to the centre of the surface to which the symbol is applied 
R	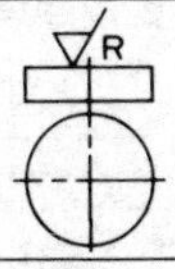	Approximately radial relative to the centre of the surface to which the symbol is applied 

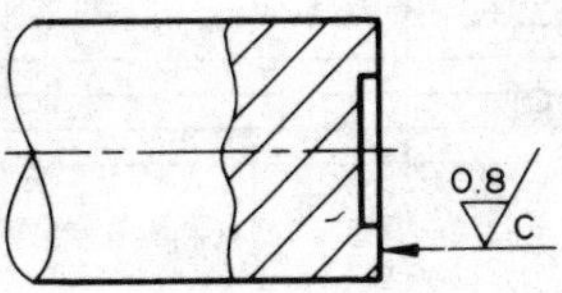

Circular lay specified by symbol

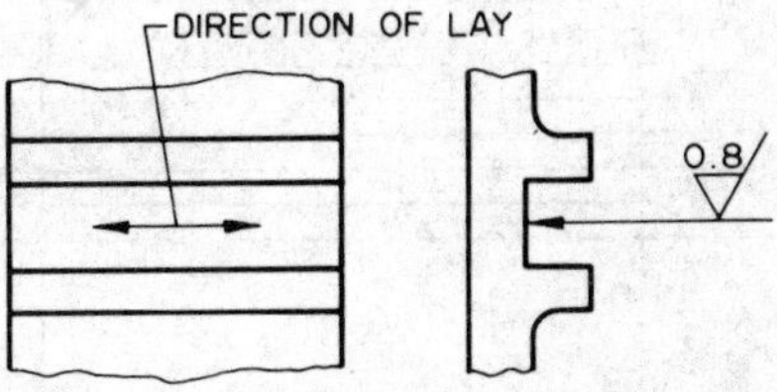

Direction of lay specified by note

Fig. 4.8 *Direction of Lay*

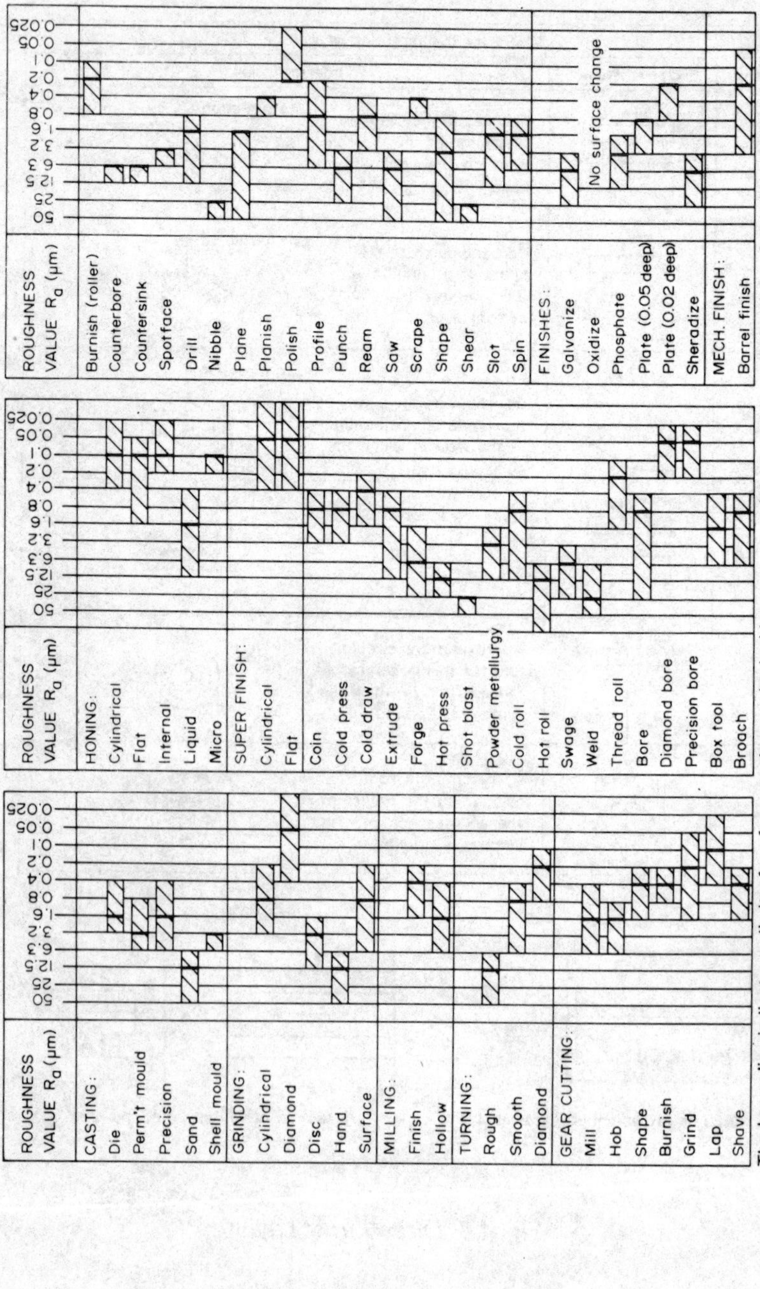

The heavy line indicates a limit of surface roughness obtainable at commercial cost. Values to the right of the line can be obtained at increased cost

Fig. 4.9 *Surface Roughness Values Obtained by Different Processes*

example specifying circular lay is given in Figure 4.8, together with an example of the use of a note, when a symbol would not make the drawing intention clear.

Surface roughness values obtained by different processes

Surfaces manufactured by the same production process will have roughness values lying between fairly well-defined upper and lower limits. The table in Figure 4.9 gives typical ranges of roughness values attainable by a number of processes. In each range, roughness values to the left of the heavy line can be achieved at a commercial cost. Values to the right of the line will require more production time and this will increase the cost of finishing the surface. In this connection BS 1134 points out that for many common machining processes, finishing costs increase steeply for roughness values below 0.4 μm R_a.

Figure 4.9 also gives typical roughness values for some chemically produced protective finishes such as galvanizing and plating. These are long-term finishes. Short-term protection is frequently applied in the form of oil, grease or a plastic film. Parts may also be finished mechanically by tumbling them with grit in a rotating barrel for a controlled time. This operation deburrs the parts and enhances the surface finish. Burrs are the sharp edges produced by machining operations and they must be removed to avoid scratching mating parts, damaging 'O' rings and seals on assembly and to prevent cut fingers when the parts are handled.

5 Computer aided design

The preceding survey of drawing office organization in chapter 2 can now be used as a basis for examining the use of *computer aided design* (CAD) in the design office.

The essential word from the abbreviated title CAD is 'aided', for at present and perhaps never, a computer cannot itself 'design'. Everything that the computer provides, depends on the individual computer software and the links between the operator and the computer. The more sophisticated the output, the more complex the *program* has to be and the more it costs. Note that in computer language the American spelling of programme is used.

Uses of CAD in the design office

CAD equipment for a design office can at present do several things (see Figure 5.1).

(1) It can *store* and *retrieve* all manner of reference data such as suppliers, materials, delivery dates, costs, material properties, tables of compared values, stressing data, formulae, previous test results, etc.; that is, it can act as a library system. Items such as those shown in Figures 2.2 and 2.6 could be edited by the computer user. Information from customers, sales and market research can be presented to help to build a brief for the designer.

(2) It can *calculate* and *predict* from known data input such things as strengths and stresses, and draw graphs, charts, etc. It can also show trends as parameters are changed. It can provide optimal *appreciations* and *comparisons* of design solutions. It can *select* and *contrast* materials. It can perform these operations faster than by any other means, but only as accurately as the programming parameters will allow. The designer can therefore investigate the available reference data, prepare a specification, analyse useful inputs

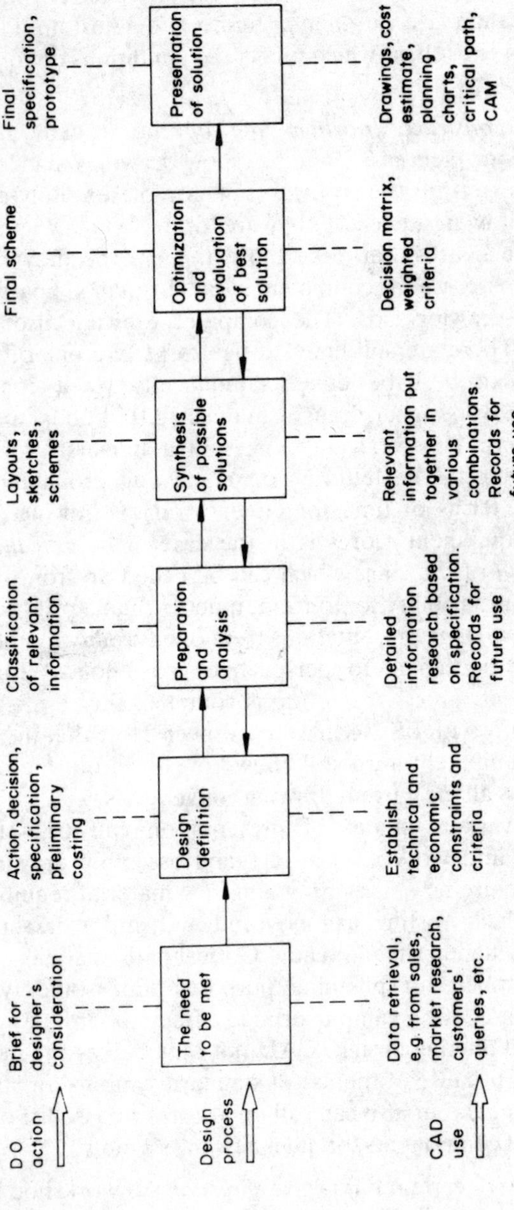

Fig. 5.1 *Cad Use in the Design Office*

in preparing possible solutions to meet the brief and evaluate how the possible solutions will meet the requirements of the specification. He can then optimize and adjust until the best solution is evolved which meets the conditions of competing criteria.

(3) It can *construct drawings* line by line in any form of projection. Figures 5.2 and 5.3 show drawings made using a Medusa set-up (by courtesy of Middlesex Polytechnic). These drawings, because they are 'drawn' via key and touch-sensitive boards, can take more time in the drawing than they would on a competent draughtsman's board using normal drawing aids. The computer drawing also has no 'style'. There are still many design tasks of a one-off nature which can best be done economically by a competent designer or designer-draughtsman using traditional methods. CAD has, however, advantages in a universal format of presentation. The lettering on a drawing probably breaks even in terms of time for either form of drawing. Where CAD equipment scores is in the ease of *modification* and *alteration* of drawings which can be called up from storage, as well as its ability to print-out quicker than a print room. It can also change presentations from one form to another, e.g. from orthographic to perspective projection. With some equipment, unless the set-up is complex, the results do not agree fully with BS 308 in every respect. Note that the user of CAD equipment must still know how to set out the drawing as well as all the current drawing conventions.

The various modes of presentation can translate the scheme into working drawings and assembly drawings for manufacture as well as providing raw material requirements from which costing can be predicted and workshop and testing schedules made ready. Critical path analyses can also be examined for planning purposes. For some types of draughting, for example printed circuit board design and pipe and ducting design, CAD not only makes the drawings quickly, because of the use of standard symbols for standard components, but also can call up a stores release list of those standard components for quickness in assembly.

(4) It can, with certain links, give *directions* to workshop tooling (*computer aided manufacture*, CAM) so that it is possible to

obtain both detail drawings and machined parts and complete assemblies from assembly drawings with the use of automatic and robotized assembly lines.

(5) Some software programs on the market are specifically arranged for artistic use by which surface contours, colours and textures can be used to produce photographic-like reproductions of three-dimensional objects in which planes and curves from mechanically produced parts can be portrayed readily. This ability can be useful to sell ideas and proposed designs to customers who cannot understand conventional engineering drawings, even to the extent of showing movement. At present, such screen pictures cannot be translated into prints like photographs but even this may be possible later.

A diagrammatic representation of one type of computer CAD set-up is shown in Figure 5.4; other systems differ in details.

Designers are increasingly subject to public criticism and legal action, therefore the designer should realize that despite the aid available from a CAD system he must understand the limitations of the software programs he has used in modelling his presentation.

Costs of CAD

For a company to invest in CAD and perhaps CADCAM requires a very careful investigation of costs. It is noticeable that in the few short years since CAD began, the equipment has altered greatly, that is to say much costly equipment has been outdated and this will doubtless continue. It has been common practice to have to add to an originally costly set-up further costly packages in order to keep abreast of progress. Then at the next 'break-through' it is found that a smaller cheaper set-up, had it been waited for, would have sufficed. Training of staff requires considerable time and, as yet, staff tend to be retrained from existing design staff, because the basic drawing conventions have to be known first.

Gradually, differing 'packages' have become available which are suitable for different sorts of design office and it is now possible to install CAD equipment at a cost which a small company can afford.

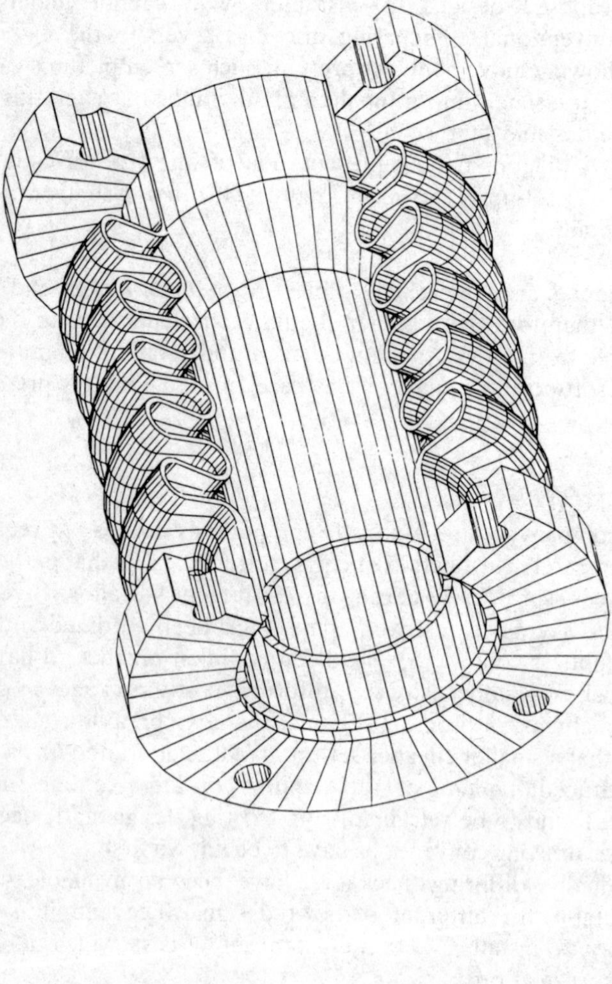

Fig. 5.2

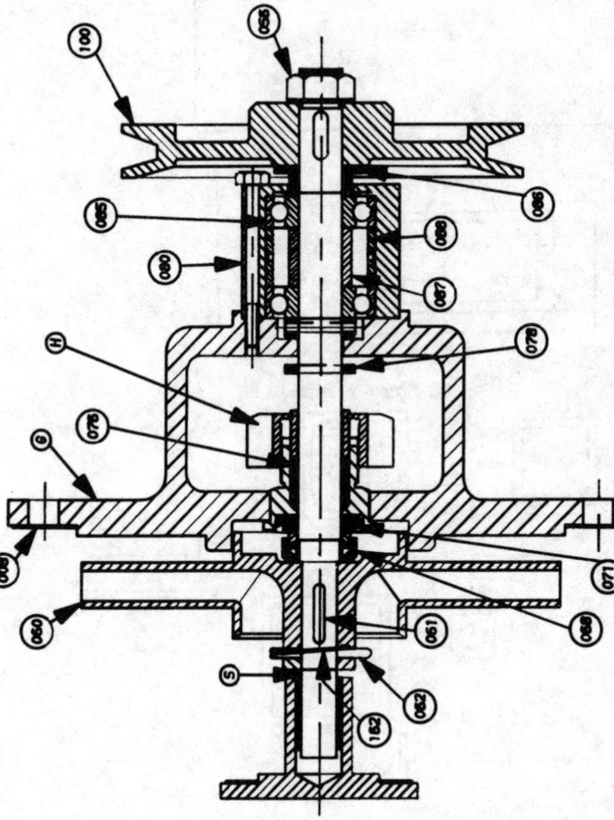
100
056
086
085
088
080
087
H
078
076
6
008
071
060
061
068
S
062
162
SECTION A-A

Fig. 5.3

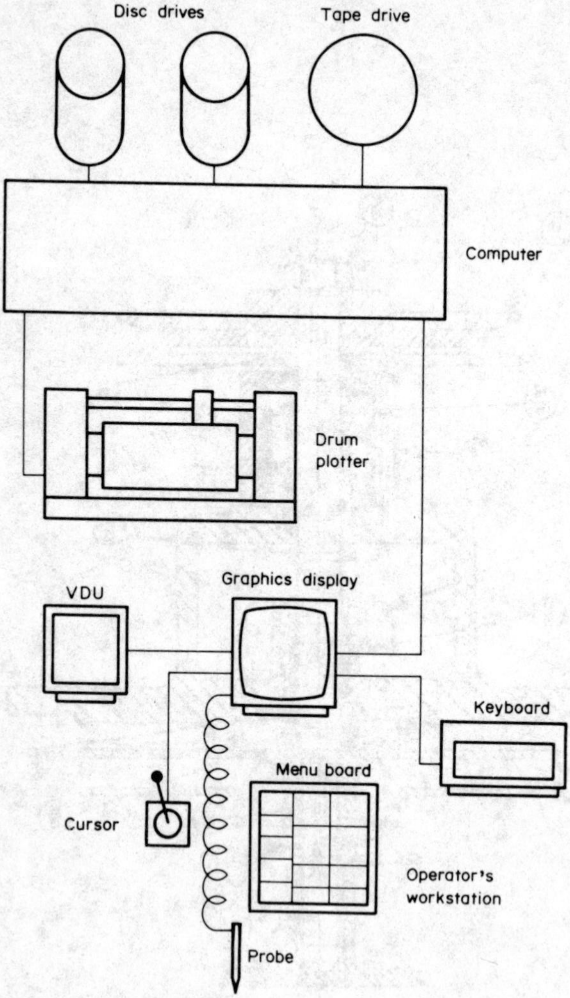

Fig. 5.4 *Diagram of a Cad System*

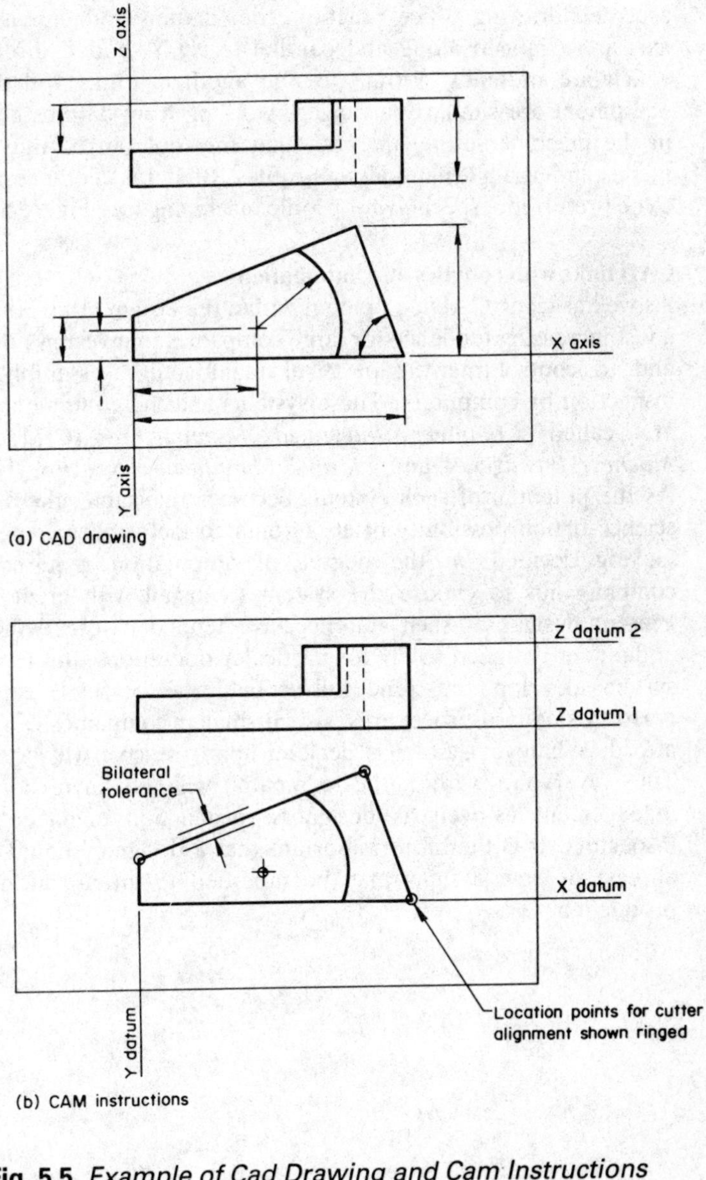

Fig. 5.5 *Example of Cad Drawing and Cam Instructions*

Dimensioning of CAD drawings

Dimensioning and tolerancing of CAD drawings follows normally accepted drawing office practices, i.e. datums and dimensional axis are arranged along and parallel to X, Y, and Z directions which are mutually normal to one another. Links with CAM equipment are similarly arranged, working from datums defined in the machine setting in order that the tool can be moved in planes and at angles and along profiles. Bilateral tolerances seem to be preferred, especially for profile machining (see Figure 5.2).

CAD links with robotics and automation

As well as using CAD equipment within the design office, there is a fast increasing tendency for large companies to invest in robotics and to control many aspects of manufacture, assembly and inspection by computers. These systems and the equipment used are called *Computer Integrated Manufacture* (CIM) and *Machine Intelligence* and *Flexible Manufacture Systems* (FMS). As the potential of such systems becomes realizable, the almost science-fiction possibility of an automated factory comes nearer. Having decided on the degree of automation required the company has to choose the system to install with great care. Present designs of such systems have tended to use dedicated equipment designed solely for particular operations, but as these systems develop, the trend will probably be for small 'cells' to perform standard procedures, which smaller companies can then afford. Whatever system is decided upon the cost will be high. Thus everyone within the company will be involved, top management as well as designers, production engineers and inspectors. It is therefore important that a designer should keep abreast of how designs may be modified to attain automated production.

6 Costs

Strategic market planning

In many organisations planning at divisional level is brought by divisional managers to company management for approval, and as long as each division appears to promise a contribution to company profitability their plans are agreed. However, managers at divisional level are protective of their divisions and see threats from other divisions. Where interrelated activities between divisions are necessary each manager tends to plan for himself. It is then probable that divisions which have possibilities of growth are starved of money while other divisions may spend unnecessarily, because if they do not spend their budget they will have a reduced budget next year.

Many organisations have now begun to accept that units or divisions within a corporation may need to grow at different rates and that they may not show the same order of profitability or require the same money input, but nevertheless contribute in an important way to the company's well-being. One reason for this change in planning is that many companies now face the fact of limited cash resources. With the recognition that internal divisions may have different objectives and roles the concept of a *business unit* has emerged and the management term *portfolio* is employed to describe an agglomeration of business units. The business unit comprises several *programme units*. These programme units represent product lines, market segments and industries to which the company sells. An organisation made up in this way is called a *matrix* organisation. The definitions of business and programme units differ in different companies but generally they are construed as units charged with particular responsibilities. The programme units comprise resources such as physical facilities, technical ability of personnel or departmental capital. The portfolio's existence in terms of business and programme units means that *strategic market plans* are drawn up for the corporation or company as a whole.

For strategic market planning each manager of a programme unit or a resource or a business unit must first decide:

(a) (i) Which customers his unit serves, how they are to be satisfied and how he will use his available technology to do so.

(ii) If and how the company differentiates customers' needs and how they are satisfied.

Defining a business therefore has implications both for the company and the customer.

(b) Expectations of sales, market share, investment return, net income and available cash.

In terms of desirability to the company, these items may conflict. A balance between them must then be struck and reviewed later, probably at intervals.

(c) When the above items are known, strategies can be formulated in detail. At this stage business, programme and resource managers interact.

(d) Finally the resources and budgets are allocated so that predictions of income, balances and cash flow can be attempted.

Many of these interactions, especially (c) and (d), are necessarily iterative and may require remixing the factors which make up that stage of consideration.

The analysis of planning

In recent times three methods for analysis have been proposed.

(i) *Portfolio analysis* in which charts with axes representing market share and industry growth are prepared. Market share is related to profitability and industry growth to capital investment. Such charts may be prepared at specific intervals for both the company and its competitors.

(ii) *Charts of business position* with axes representing the attractiveness of the market versus the strength of the company position within the market. These charts help in judging possible investment.

(iii) PIMS (*profit impact of market strategy*), a model system based on an analysis of many companies by the authors Schoeffer, Buzzell and Heany (Harvard Business Review), in which strategic variables and situation variables are used to determine which strategies work best under which market conditions.

Cost estimation

The usual way of costing a product is to consider the total cost for the company to make the product as the sum of direct and indirect costs. The *direct costs* are those specifically attributable to the product and comprise:

(a) *raw material costs* for sheet, bar, castings, forgings, etc., and bought-out items such as screw fasteners and bearings;

(b) *direct labour costs* arising from setting, machining, tooling, testing and inspection, packaging, etc.

The *indirect costs* are made up of:

(a) *indirect labour and material costs* such as those for stores and cleaning and consumable materials such as lubricants;

(b) *administration costs* for office services and labour, office materials, upkeep of office machines, etc., and the costs of the personnel, salaries, training and medical departments;

(c) *sales costs* incurred in marketing such as the production of sales brochures and sales representatives' travel and expenses and the cost of servicing and meeting warranty claims by customers.

The allocation of indirect costs will depend on company policy. It might be a standard pro-rata on-cost according to numbers of parts produced, or it might perhaps be loaded more on a popular item.

Figure 6.1 shows how total cost is related to production and material costs and indirect costs, and how the cost to the company can vary with numbers produced for a particular product. Production costs fall with increasing numbers produced because, for example, the expenditure for tooling and machines can be amortized over larger numbers whereas material and indirect costs rise with increasing numbers produced because, for example, more material is used.

A simple way of estimating the points in the launch of a new product where the company emerges from loss to profit relative to the number or volume of that product produced and sold is by use of the *break-even point*. This is illustrated in Figure 6.2.

If profit, i.e. total sales income minus total costs, is plotted

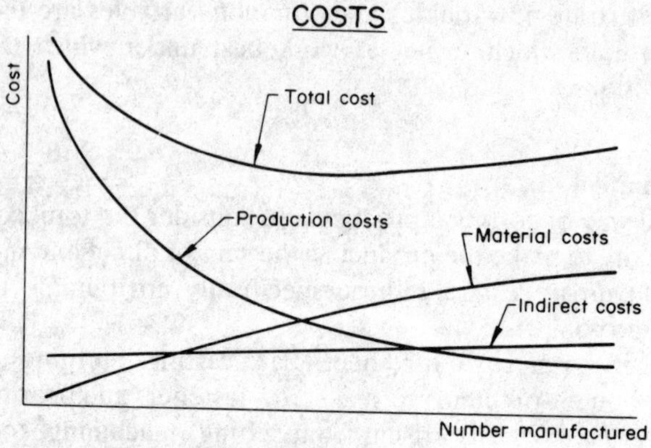

Fig. 6.1 *Effect of Output on Costs*

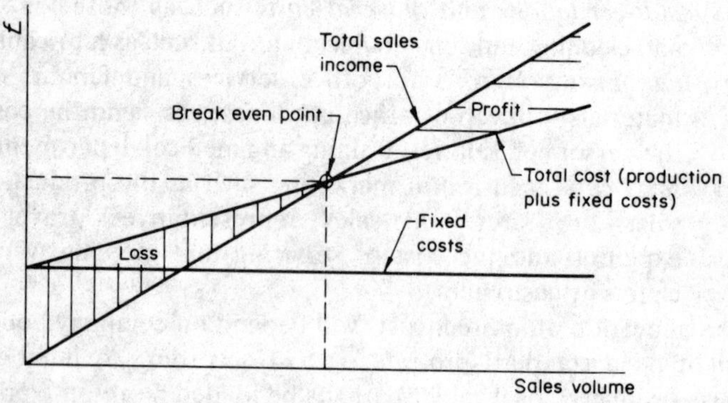

Fig. 6.2 *Break Even Point Between Profit and Loss*

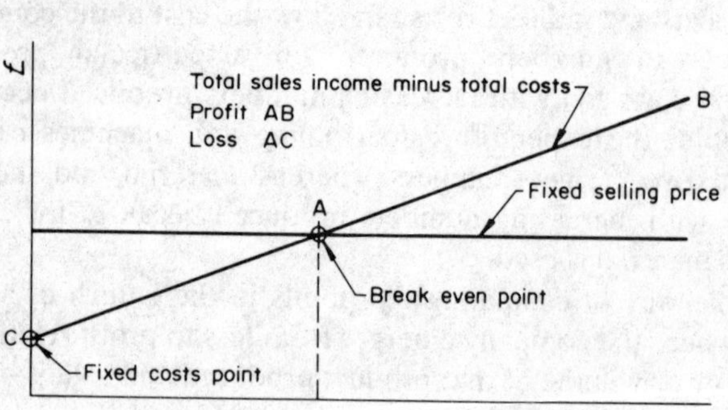

Fig. 6.3 *Fixed Selling Price and Break Even Point*

against a fixed selling price, it can be seen from Figure 6.3 that alteration of the selling price will affect the break-even point relative to profit. Raising the selling price raises the break-even point and vice versa.

In Figure 6.4, graphs to find the break-even points for two products A and B are plotted on the same axes, these graphs being similar to that in Figure 6.2. From Figure 6.4 it is possible to determine which product is the more profitable for a specific output, in this case 15 000 units.

Design and technical merit

If various solutions of the design brief are examined then it is possible to estimate (usually on the basis of past company activities) both manufacturing and selling costs and to rate these against the *technical merit* of the various solutions. Technical merit might be assessed in terms of quality, reliability, complexity, etc.

From these considerations, curves such as those shown in Figure 6.5 emerge. This figure shows that if technical merit is low, selling costs will be high, which can lead to a loss. The marketing department will have to put more effort into persuading customers to buy the product, which, although within its general specification, may not come up to their expectations. This, in turn, may lead to more customer complaints resulting in more time being spent by the sales force and the servicing and warranty departments. To avoid loss of goodwill it may be necessary to offer special discounts, replacements and improved servicing arrangements. All these effects of low technical merit reduce the profitability of the product.

On the other hand, too high a level of technical merit will also reduce the profitability of the product, since the total costs will rise with the inevitable increase in production costs. More time will probably be needed for manufacture and inspection, it may be necessary to use labour which is more highly skilled on more expensive equipment, and scrap and reworking are likely to increase.

There are, therefore, upper and lower limits of technical merit outside which profit from the product becomes a loss. Within these limits, as Figure 6.5 shows, there is a range of technical merit which maximizes the profit. The design selected for manufacture should fall within this range.

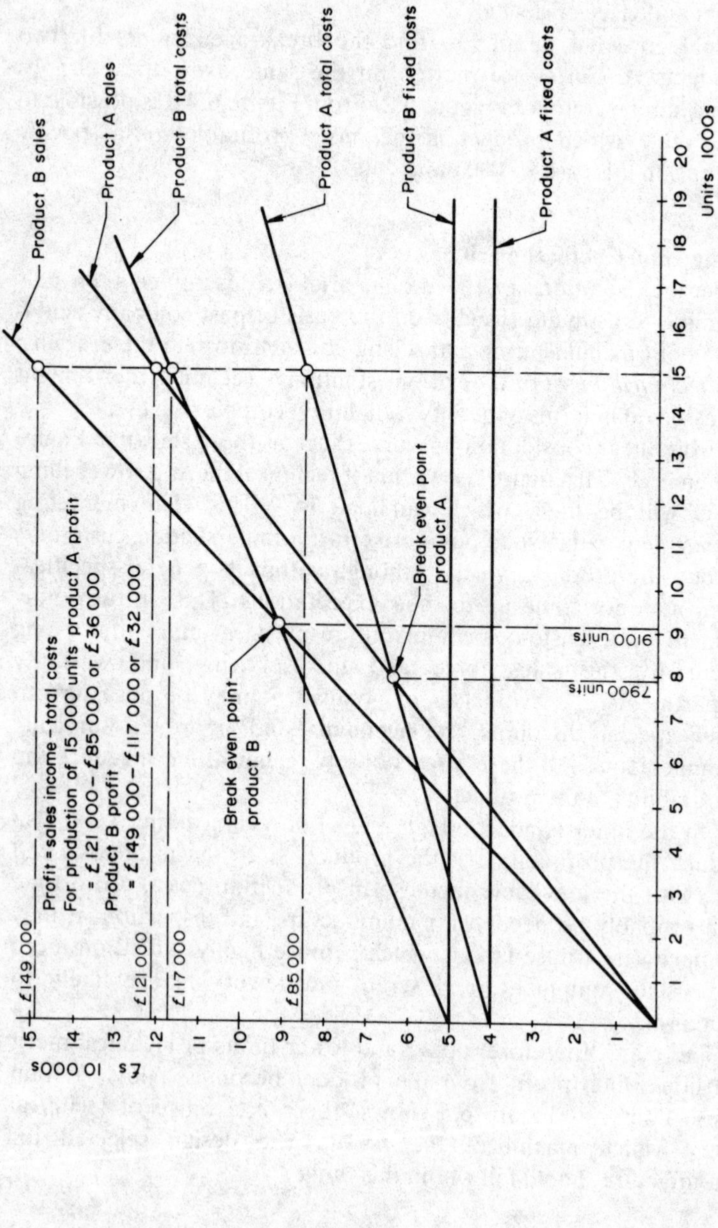

Fig. 6.4 *Profit Comparison – Same Production of Two Products*

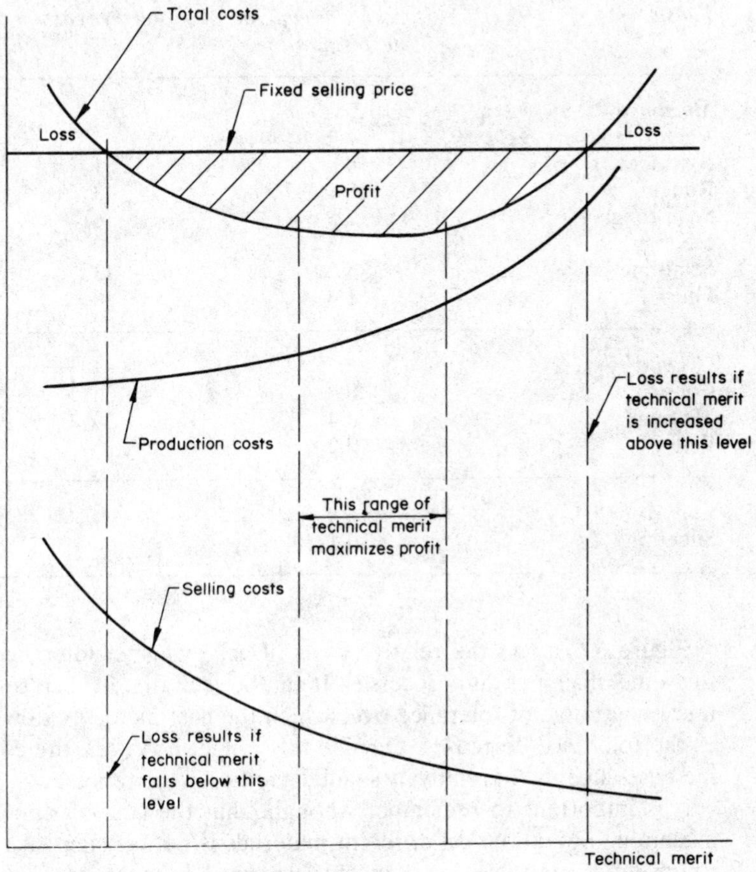

Fig. 6.5 *Effect of Technical Merit on Costs and Profit*

Effect of finish and tolerances on costs

In chapter 4, Figure 4.9 points out that making use of a particular method of machining to obtain an extra fine finish may prove uneconomical. The relative costs of increasingly fine finishes are shown in the following table.

Finish	*Surface, texture micrometres (μm)*	*Relative costs*
Machined		
Very rough (very coarse feed)	50	1
Rough	25	3
Semi-rough	12.5	6
Medium	6.3	9
Semi-fine	3.2	13
Fine	1.6	18
Ground		
Coarse	0.8	20
Medium	0.4	30
Fine	0.2	35
Lapped		
Super fine	0.1	40

Figure 6.6 shows the relative costs of achieving set tolerances for some machines and processes. It can be seen that in each case there is a range of tolerance over which the cost increases slowly as the tolerance decreases. Outside this range, however, the cost increases steeply for relatively small decreases in tolerance.

It is important to remember, though, that the cost of similar machining operations on different materials is not constant. As a rough guide, if the cost of machining dural is taken as 1, the relative cost of the same machining on mild steel is about 2, on stainless steel it is about 2.8 and on nimonic it is about 5.1.

Value engineering and value analysis

It should now be apparent that in meeting a brief the designer

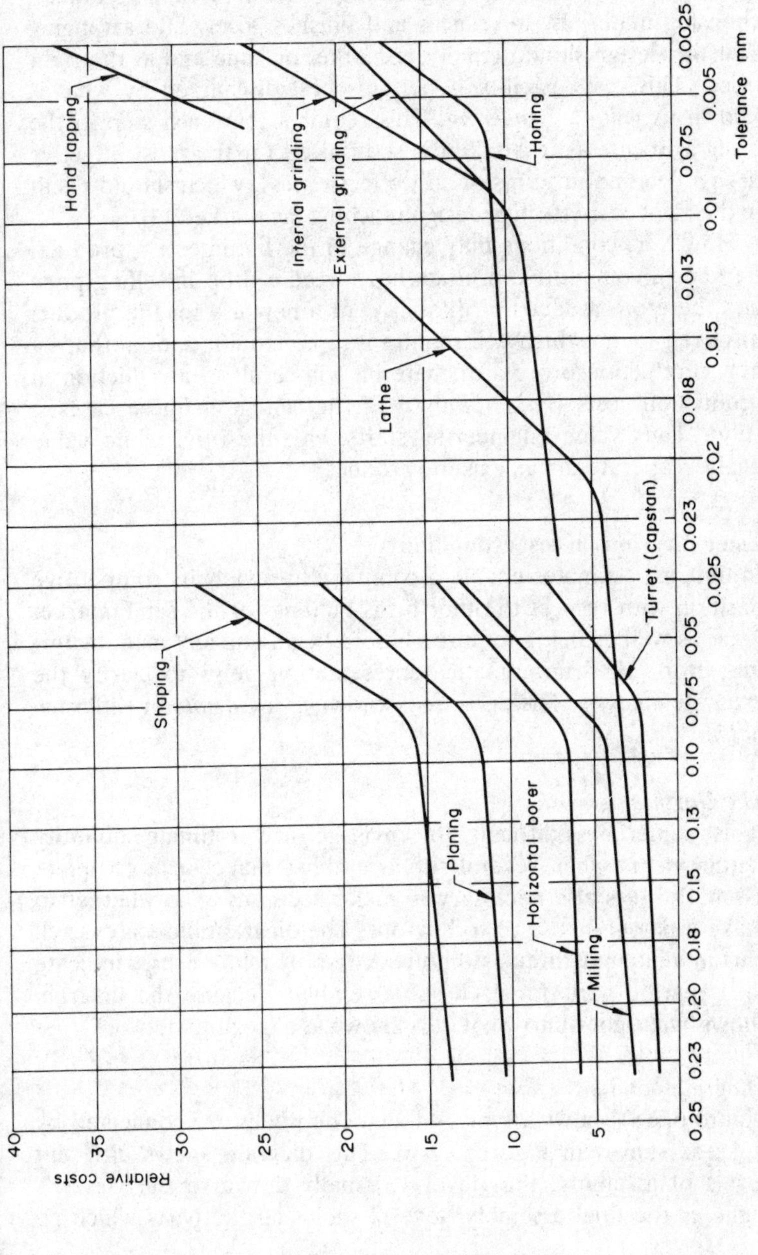

Fig. 6.6 *Cost of Achieving Set Tolerances for Some Machines and Processes*

bears considerable responsibility not only for producing ideas quickly but also for conveying his requirements clearly to others, choosing materials, tolerances and finishes wisely and arranging that the design should reach the market on time and at the right price. This responsibility is perhaps best discharged by what is known as *value engineering*. This requires that each step in the design process as it is taken is scrutinized for the most effective design decision in terms of cost effectiveness, which should result in the most cost-effective design reaching the market.

However, conditions may change in the lifetime of a product. Perhaps a competitive product has forced a drop in selling price and therefore reduced profitability, or a new use for the product has been found which will require it to be modified, or perhaps a new production process or material will result in a reduction in production costs. *Value analysis* of the change in these cases is valid. Thus value engineering starts with the brief while value analysis operates on an existing product.

Using diagrams in cost estimation

Initial cost estimates enable a company to review its competitive position with respect to other firms bidding for the same market area, as well as being required before beginning any manufacturing effort. A diagrammatic representation helps to clarify the estimate analysis. The diagram is known as a *Gozinto* or **explosion** network.

The Gozinto network

It is sometimes difficult to envisage and estimate quantity requirements when several sub-assemblies make up a complete assembly. It is also necessary to make decisions as to whether to make a part in-house or to buy-out. The diagram illustrates each part in a manufactured assembly. Assembly relationships indicate the separate parts for each sub-assembly. Because the diagram shows 'what-goes-into-what' it is known as a Gozinto network.

Diagram notation

Figure 6.7(a) shows a typical node. The nodes are connected by links as shown in Figure 6.7(b). This diagram shows different levels of assembly; thus level 1, usually drawn to the viewer's right, is the final assembly; level 2 shows all the parts which go

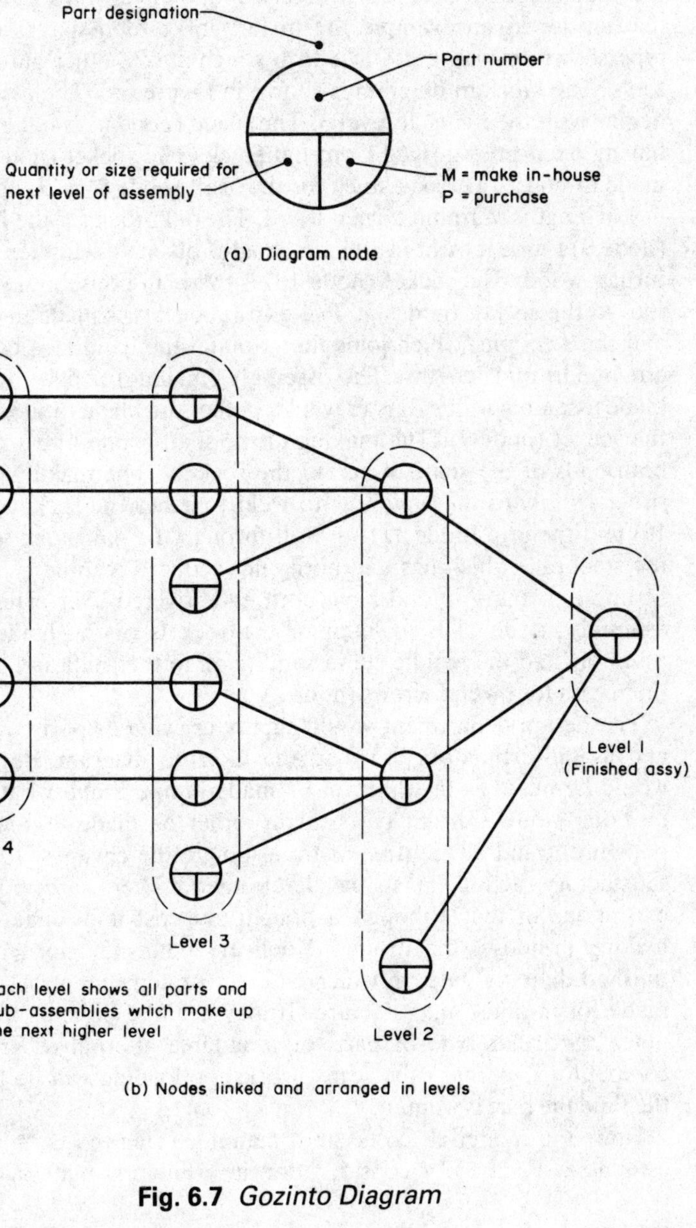

Fig. 6.7 *Gozinto Diagram*

into and make up the assembly in level 1. Level 2 nodes may be sub-assemblies, in which case level 3 indicates all the parts which make up the sub-assemblies in level 2 and so on leftward.

Consider as an example the making of garden spades of the type shown in Figure 6.8 at a firm which makes other gardening tools. The Gozinto diagram is shown in Figure 6.8. The assembly begins with the items at level 3. The blade (node 6) is bought-out having been press forged from flat stock. The socket (node 7) is made in-house. The oak stock for the shaft (node 8) is bought-out in 1 m lengths of round turned wood. The oak stock for the handle (node 9) is bought-out in 100 mm lengths of small diameter round turned wood. The socket (node 10) is made in-house in a similar tool to the socket (node 7). The grip (node 11) is made in-house and the steel pin, which joins the grip and the handle, is bought-out in 110 mm lengths. The assembly (making) activity for the blade assembly (node 2) is to weld together the blade (node 6) and the socket (node 7). The making of the shaft (node 4) is to taper both ends of the shaft to accept the sockets. The making of the sub-assembly of the handle is to weld together the socket (node 10) and the grip (node 11); to drill through the oak stock so that the steel pin, which has had both ends reduced, can be inserted, sprung into the grip and have both ends riveted over. The final assembly (node 1) is to hammer the sockets of the blade sub-assembly and the handle sub-assembly on to the shaft and secure them with four wood screws (node 3).

The design department would supply drawing or part numbers and as the estimators draw up the Gozinto diagram, decisions would be made as to what can be made in-house and what must be bought-out. Certain parts might either be made in-house or bought-out and at the time of the estimate the cheapest form of satisfactory action must be determined. There are possible exceptions in that although a bought-out cost may under-price making in-house, the promised delivery date may not suit the finished delivery date; in which case a cost adjustment has to be made for in-house manufacture. It may even be possible to buy-out a particular type of part, or a suitable alternative, from a competitor if perhaps the firm's workshop loading will be full at the time the part is wanted.

Now the material costs and manufacturing costs may be estimated. Factors for consideration in estimating material costs

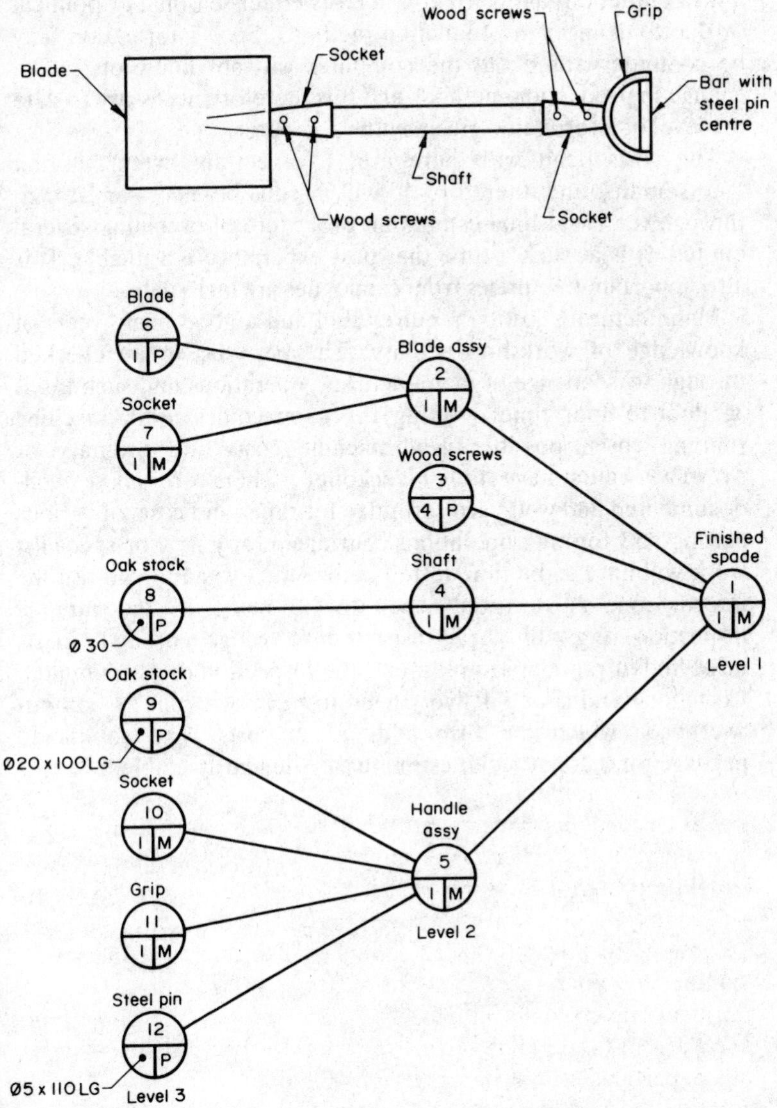

Fig. 6.8 *Gozinto Diagram for Spade*

are: quantity required; previous similar orders; time required for a firm quotation; and variation in costs either seasonal or political or due to changes in production methods. Such information may be computer-stored but the computer will not know of, say, a change in production methods and it is therefore necessary to date the level of information given by the computer.

The costs dealt with here are, to a certain extent, a first 'guesstimate' and therefore it will hardly be necessary to go through the usual final estimating procedure of obtaining several quotes. It is at such a time that past experience is valuable. It is also important that prices from catalogues are up to date.

Manufacturing costing requires skill and a good many years of knowledge of workshop activity. The part has to be checked through its sequence of manufacturing operations and such items as floor-to-floor times, setting times, machines used, machine running costs, possible new machine costs and ordinary or overtime hours have to be reckoned. There are many well-documented and well-used formulae for times and costs of various cutting and forming operations, but again, any new or specialist work will have to be time-tested before the estimator can use the information. A decision needs to be made of the rate of inspection, e.g. all parts inspected to gauge, or 10% parts inspected in random samples, and the inspection costs estimated. Costs for packing and delivery need to be known plus the various overheads which the firm adds as on-costs. The completed package for that particular estimate can then be assembled.

7 Design exercises

These exercises are based on the preceding text. Some cover more than one topic; others require some research or reference to other material, such as British Standards, for their solution.

All dimensions on the figures are in millimetres. Drawings and sketches for solutions may be drawn in first or third angle projection to suitable scales. Omitted dimensions should be estimated using engineering judgement.

The exercises should be worked in a professional manner with drawings and sketches of high quality and clearly laid out calculations.

Xerox copies needed for solutions should, if possible, be enlargements of the given figures.

1 Figure 7.1 shows a cranked lever. Interpret the given views and draw section A–A only with the following additions:
  (a) On centre X show a standard M16 stud to BS 4439, with a nominal length of 50 mm. The metal end length of the stud is not to be greater than the thickness of the lever.
  (b) On centre Y show a through M12 tapped hole.
  (c) Show a shaft with a tapered end 50 mm long, secured to the lever with two M24 thin units to BS 3692 and a plain bright washer, normal diameter, Form A, to BS 4320. The shaft carries a Woodruff key of 14 mm radius.

  The stud should point in the opposite direction to the shaft taper. No hidden detail or dimensions are required.

2 Set out the detailing procedure used in a drawing office from the receipt of a scheme drawing from the designer through the various drawings needed to order material, produce parts, use standard parts and assemble the machine.
  Produce a sketch of one of the drawings, including the border, title block, projection symbol, etc.

3 (a) List 16 likely requirements which may be included in a design specification for a battery-operated torch.

(b) Write typical design specification clauses for four of these requirements under separate headings. Refer to BSI publication PD 6112.

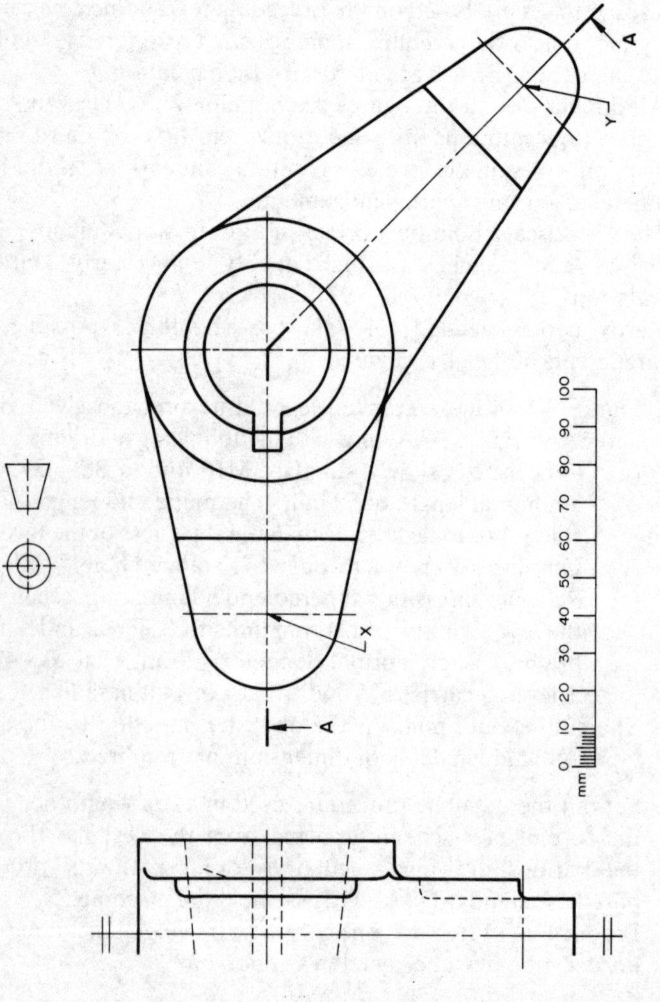

Fig. 7.1

(c) List in order of importance suitable criteria for evaluating alternative designs for the torch and explain how the relative importance of the criteria is influenced by circumstances.

4 You are the chief draughtsman of a small drawing office and have four draughtsmen, one junior and a typist/clerk in your charge. All printing is done, when required, by a trade printer nearby. The company has recently expanded rapidly. Space is now available, after purchase of a neighbouring property, to construct a single larger drawing office to accommodate eighteen staff excluding yourself. A print machine is considered to be essential. Five new staff are to be engaged as soon as possible and the remainder in eighteen months' time, if expansion continues.

Outline your plans to meet the situation under the headings of:

(a) staff, their seniority and responsibilities;
(b) systems and organisation;
(c) equipment and layout.

5 Arrange the following stages of problem-solving in a logical sequence: evaluation; analysis; presentation; definition; synthesis; recognition.

Apply the result as a method for designing the front fork of a moped. A typical required part is shown by solid lines in Figure 7.2.

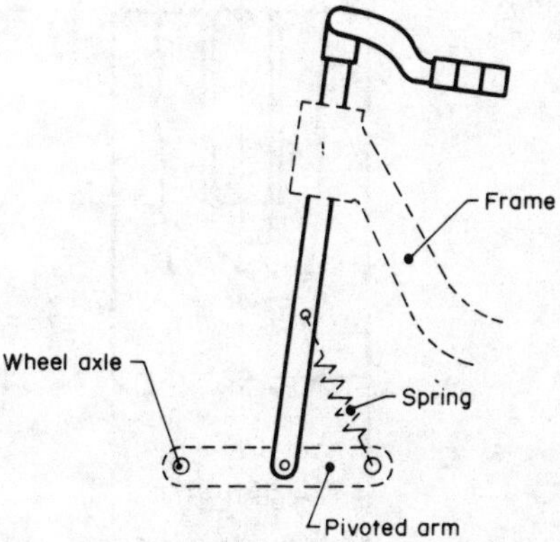

Fig. 7.2

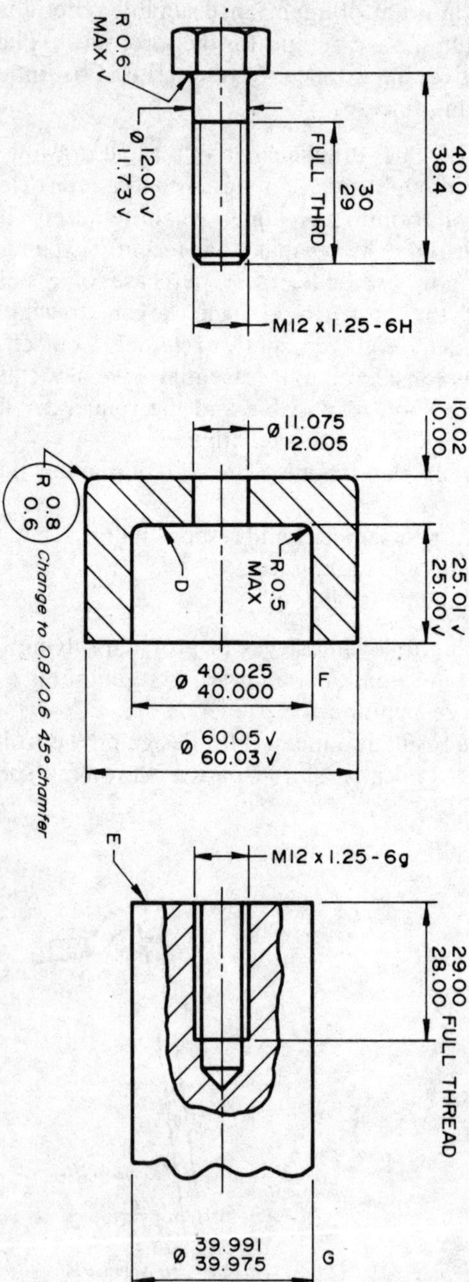
R 0.6
MAX √
Ø 12.00 √
11.73 √
FULL THRD
30
29
40.0
38.4
M12 x 1.25 - 6H
Ø 11.075
12.005
10.02
10.00
R 0.8
0.6
Change to 0.8/0.6 45° chamfer
D
R 0.5
MAX
25.01 √
25.00 √
Ø 40.025
40.000
F
Ø 60.05 √
60.03 √
E
M12 x 1.25 - 6g
29.00
28.00 FULL THREAD
Ø 39.991
39.975
G

Fig. 7.3

6 A checker is expected to find errors in dimensioning and presentation of a drawing. He notes them in coloured pencil on a print of the drawing before returning the print to the draughtsman for correction.
The design requirements for the parts shown in Figure 7.3 are that surfaces D and E should be held tightly together and that diameters F and G should be a close clearance fit. A standard bolt, as shown, holds the parts together.
Take a Xerox print of Figure 7.3 and continue checking the drawing in the manner shown, ticking all correct dimensions and features and noting all errors on the print.

7 Figure 7.4 shows a bearing bush assembly supporting a shaft. The bush fails in service because the alignment of the grease holes in the bearing and bush (which are drilled on assembly) cannot be guaranteed after a period of running. The service department suggests that a grease groove should be machined in the bush, coinciding with the existing hole.

(a) Describe a typical modification procedure to implement the change.

(b) Show a specimen of the special note required.

(c) Sketch the revised part including, without sizes, all necessary dimensions and notes.

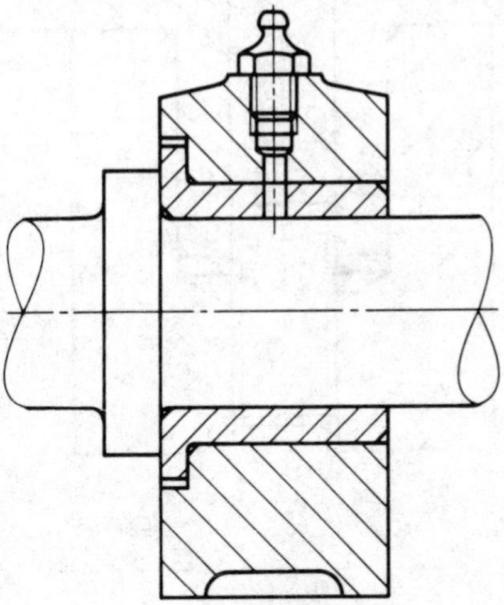

Fig. 7.4

8 Figure 7.5 shows an assembly for a rotating turntable, the parts of which are arranged as follows:
The turntable (item 2) rotates on the centre piece (item 1) which is located in the cross piece (item 3) by a spigot. The centre piece is retained by an M20 bolt (item 4).
An H8/f7 fit is required between items 1 and 2, and an H7/f6 fit is required between items 1 and 3.
Make a dimensioned drawing of item 1 only. The given figure may be scaled. All dimensions should carry suitable tolerances. Show any necessary chamfers to aid assembly and any necessary minimum radii to aid production. Complete the drawing with a border, title, scale and projection symbol.

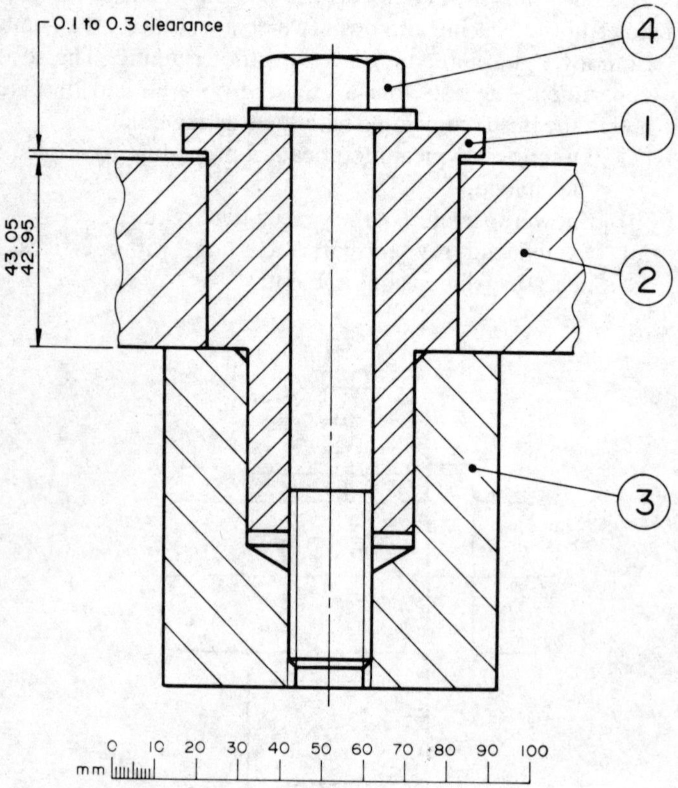

Fig. 7.5

9 Figure 7.6 shows a hinged cover attached to a casting. All parts are steel. The pivot pin has a basic size of 8 mm diameter and is to be an interference fit in the lug on the casting and a clearance fit in the lugs on the cover.

(a) Determine suitable limits of size for the pivot pin, the hole in the casting lug and the holes in the cover lugs.

(b) Make sketches of the cover and casting showing all functional dimensions without sizes.

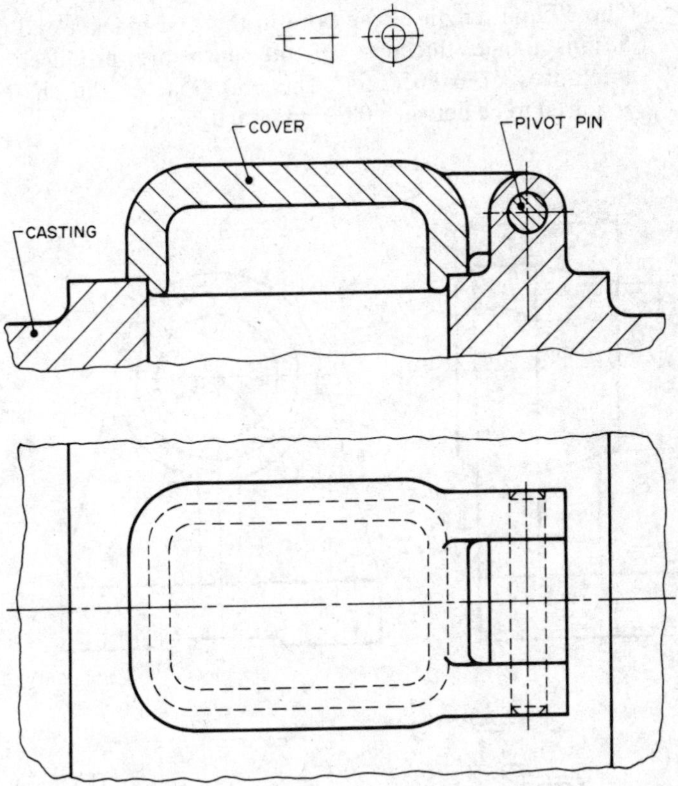

Fig. 7.6

10 Parts of a small assembly, extracted from the scheme drawing, are shown in Figure 7.7. The shaft is to rotate in the bearing bushes which are press fitted into the bore of the bracket. Basic sizes are given.

Make fully dimensioned detail drawings of the bush and the shaft to a scale of 2:1. Apply specific tolerances where necessary; a general tolerance of ±0.1 mm may be used. Show suitable chamfers and radii where required.

Notes:

Complete the shaft with a suitable length of M16 thread and a 2 mm wide undercut so that a 40 mm outside diameter plain washer and two thin lock nuts can retain the shaft in the bushes.

The 40 mm length of the bore in the cast bracket and the 5 mm flange thickness of the bush are produced to tolerances of ±0.05 mm. The end float of the shaft is required to be between 0.02 mm and 0.35 mm.

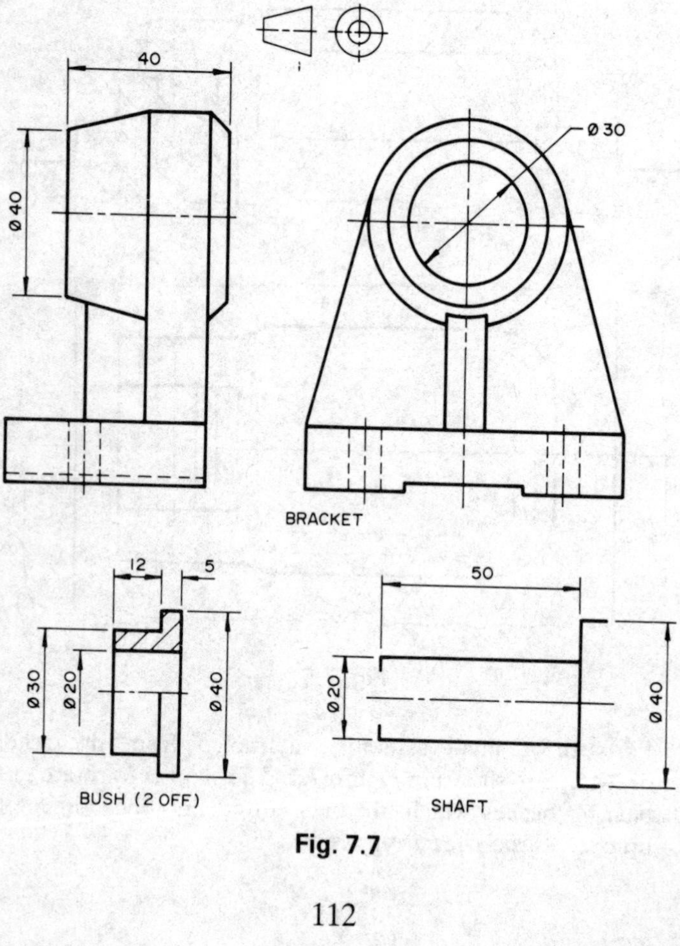

Fig. 7.7

Dimensioning, conventions, etc., are to be in accordance with the recommendations of BS 308.

11 Figure 7.8 shows an aluminium alloy housing with two identical bronze bushes pressed in which support a shaft. The shaft has a bearing diameter of 29.980/29.959 mm. The collar faces F of the shaft assembly, which establish its axial position, are 70.05/69.95 mm apart when assembled and tightened up. The axial float of the shaft is required to be 0.45/0.05 mm.

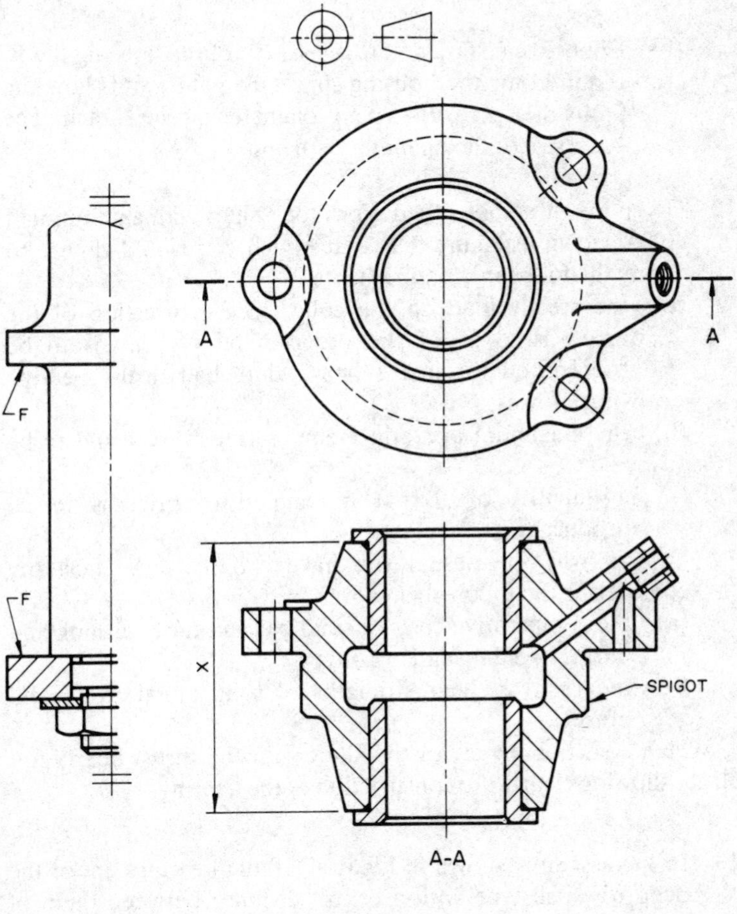

Fig. 7.8

(a) Sketch clearly and in good proportion one bush and the housing separately, in sufficient detail only to show the following dimensions:
   (i) the limits of size for the outer and inner diameters of the bush, given that the fit between the bush and housing is to be H7/p6, and the basic size of the outer diameter is 37 mm;
   (ii) the limits of size for dimension X across the housing, given that the thickness of the flange of each bush is 3.05/2.95 mm;
   (iii) the limits of size for the diameter of the bore in the housing.

(b) Choose and state below the sketch of the housing the fit required for the housing spigot diameter, and show the limits of size for the spigot diameter on the sketch. The basic size of the diameter is 70 mm.

12 Given the three possible designs for a shaft with an abutment collar shown in Figure 7.9, state which you would choose to satisfy the following requirements:
(a) the steady load on the collar in the direction of the arrow is to be of the order of 60 kN and is to be transmitted through a heavy duty ball thrust bearing (not shown);
(b) the maximum operating temperature is expected to be 120°C;
(c) a quantity of 100 at a competitive price is to be produced.

Explain why the design you have chosen is the best, by considering the following factors:
(a) the comparative costs of solid bar and tube, turning and boring, welding and brazing;
(b) the relative shear strengths of solid metal, weld and braze.

Sketch a sectional view of the shaft with the thrust bearing in place, showing clearly the construction of the bearing.

13 In the assembly shown in Figure 7.10 the bearings are of the deep row ball type with a centre distance between them of 110 mm. A wheel, fixed to the outer end of the shaft, has to

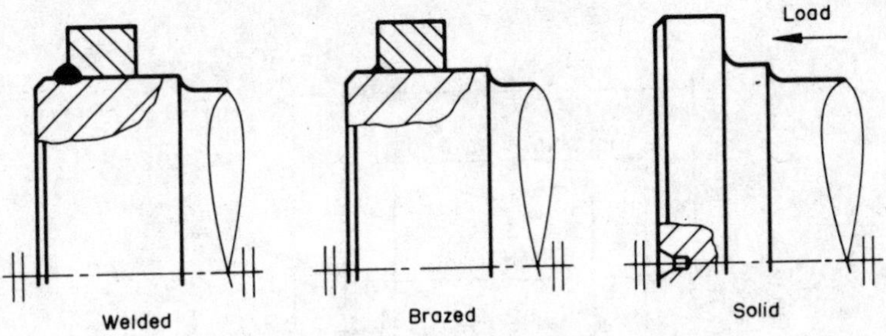

Fig. 7.9

be accurately located relative to the left-hand bearing.

Fifty machines to which the assembly is fitted are already in service. Complaints have arrived from twenty customers reporting failure of the bearings. The research and development department has found that the failure is caused by differential expansion of the shaft and sleeve during the working cycle of the machine. A check reveals that 5000 bearings are in stock and the next batch of 250 components is about to be manufactured.

(a) From a Xerox print of Figure 7.10 trace what is needed to produce a design change/salvage drawing. Include an amendment panel on the drawing.

(b) List the sequence of events needed to rectify the difficulty.

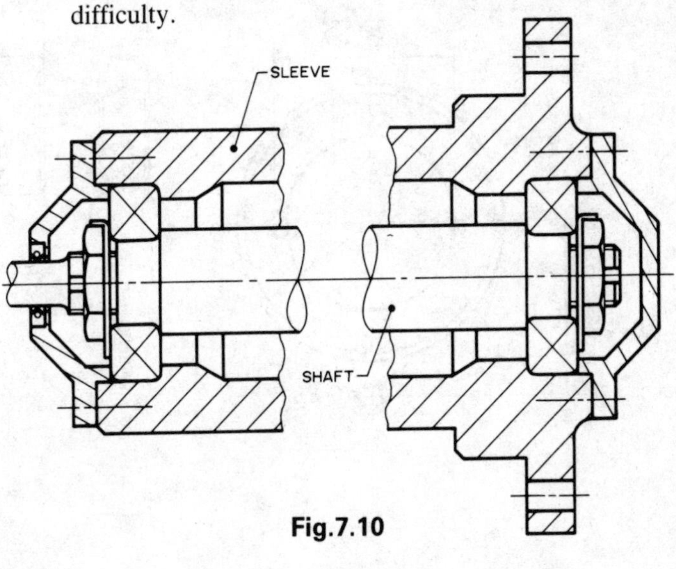

Fig.7.10

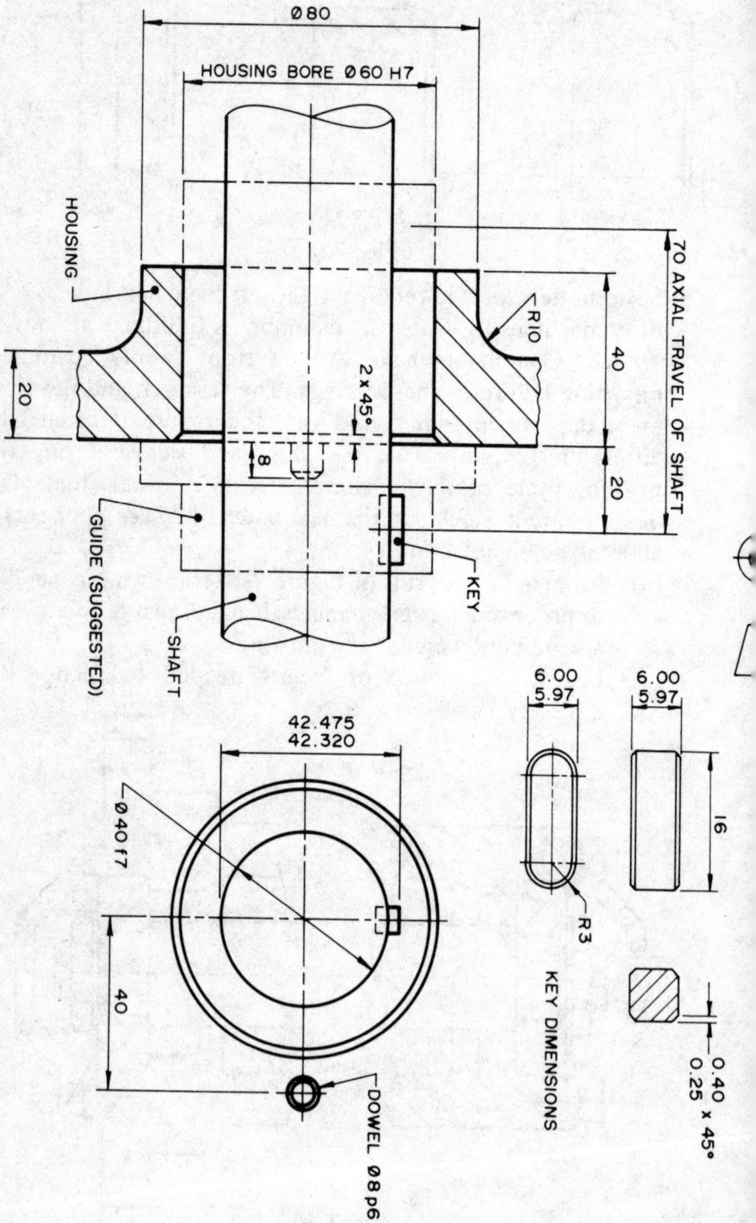

Ø80
HOUSING BORE Ø60 H7
HOUSING
70 AXIAL TRAVEL OF SHAFT
R10
40
20
2 x 45°
8
20
GUIDE (SUGGESTED)
KEY
SHAFT
42.475
42.320
Ø40 f7
40
DOWEL Ø8p6
6.00
5.97
6.00
5.97
16
R3
KEY DIMENSIONS
0.40
0.25 x 45°

Fig. 7.11

14 Figure 7.11 shows a shaft passing through a housing. A guide, a suggested outline for which is shown in double-dashed line, is to support the shaft and allow it axial movement. The shaft is fitted with a standard feather key as shown, which is to be used in conjunction with the guide to prevent the shaft rotating during its axial movement.
The orientation of the key is important. The dowel projecting from the housing can be used to prevent rotation of the guide and to assist in orientation.
Produce a fully dimensioned drawing of the guide only, incorporating features to satisfy the above requirements. Give specific tolerances where applicable. General tolerances may be taken as ±0.2 mm. Only one assembly is required. The housing cannot be altered in any way.

15 Using instruments, trace the sectional view of the steel casting, item 1, from a Xerox print of Figure 7.12.
(a) Using the traced view and any other views projected from it that you consider necessary, show all the functional dimensions for the casting. Use any conventions from BS 308 which will reduce the drawing time. Numerical values for dimensions are not required, except those specified in (b).
(b) Determine the limits of size for the two basic diameters shown in the figure and add them to the drawing in the manner recommended by BS 308.

16 Figure 7.13 shows a pictorial representation and a part sectional view of a gear reduction unit. Part A, which is repeated on the other side of the unit, is the housing for the tapered roller bearing and the housing spigot fits in a bore in the main casing. Part B, the gear hub, is an interference (press) fit in part C, the replaceable gear ring.
The drive shaft passes through the bore in part B and the drive is transmitted by a standard feather key to BS 4235: Part 1. The bearings and seals are standard items for which the chief dimensions are given. The seatings for the inner bearing races are to be finished to an R_a value of 1.6 μm. The inner races are required to have an interference fit on part B between 0.0125 mm and 0.0625 mm. Part B is made from 070M20 steel, forged, annealed and normalized.

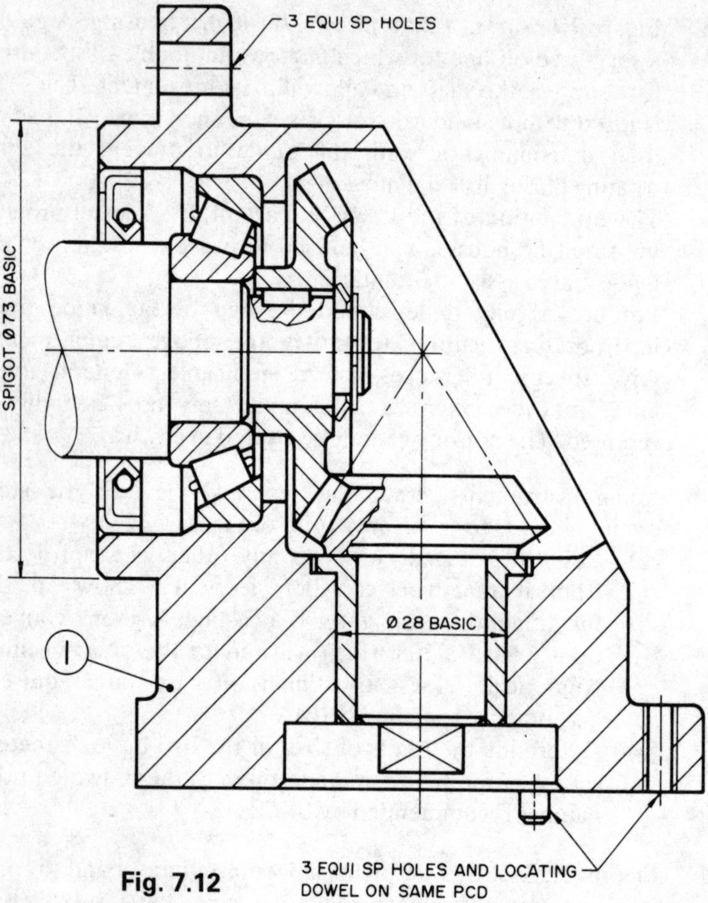

Fig. 7.12

Make a fully dimensioned and toleranced detail drawing of part B only. Suitable values for tolerances and surface finishes, other than those specified above, may be assumed. Sizes not given may be scaled from the figure. Dimensioning, conventions, etc., are to be in accordance with the recommendations of BS 308.

Particular attention should be paid to the following:

(a) the number of views needed to describe fully the gear hub;
(b) the functional dimensions;
(c) a method of separating parts B and C when part C is removed and replaced.

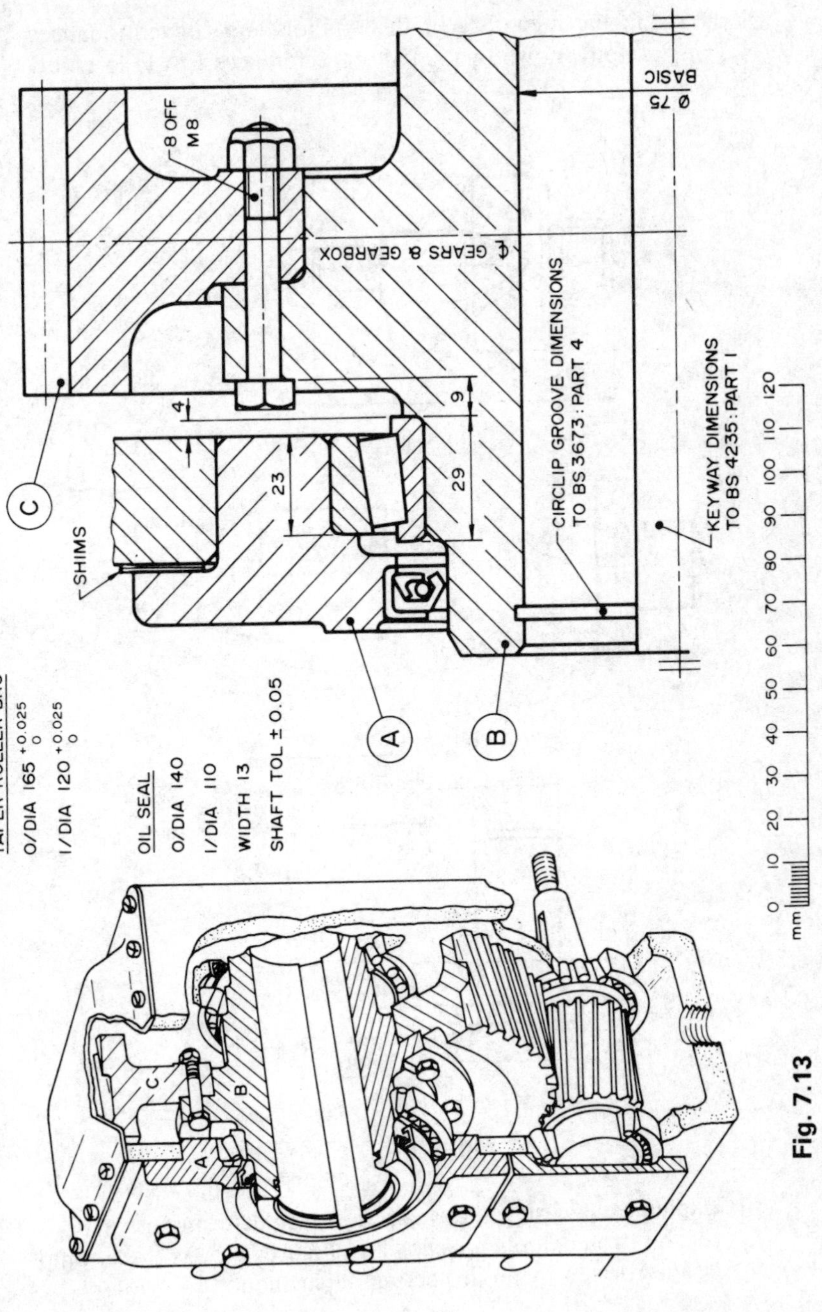
TAPER ROLLER BRG
O/DIA 165 +0.025 0
I/DIA 120 +0.025 0
OIL SEAL
O/DIA 140
I/DIA 110
WIDTH 13
SHAFT TOL ± 0.05
SHIMS
C
A
B
8 OFF M8
4
23
29
9
℄ GEARS & GEARBOX
CIRCLIP GROOVE DIMENSIONS TO BS 3673: PART 4
KEYWAY DIMENSIONS TO BS 4235: PART I
Ø 75 BASIC
mm 0 10 20 30 40 50 60 70 80 90 100 110 120

Fig. 7.13

17 Explain the meanings of the symbols and conventionalized instructions shown by the balloon references 1 to 12 in Figure 7.14.

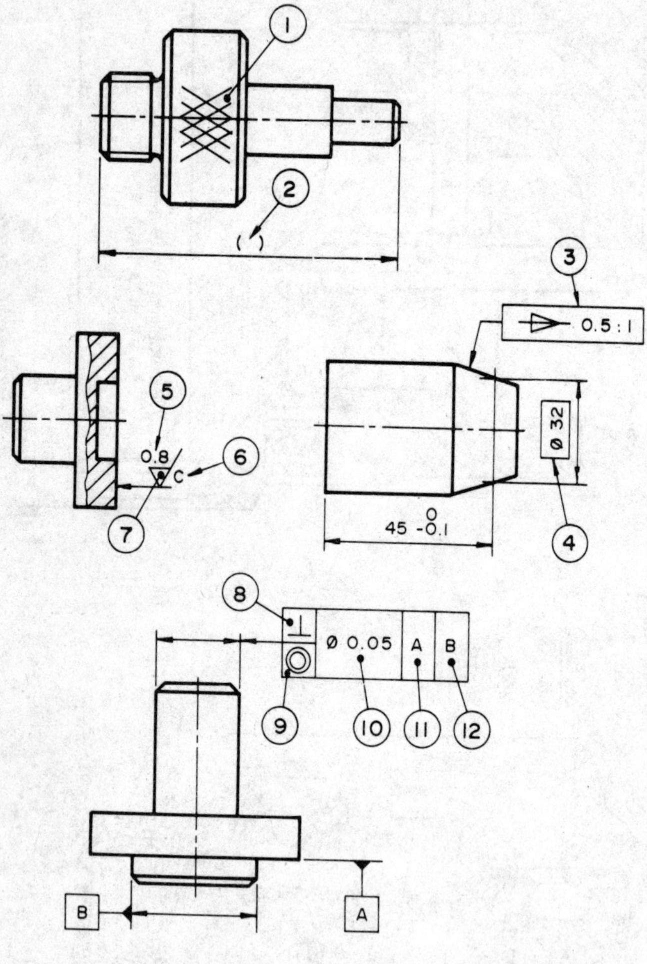

Fig. 7.14

18 Explain fully, using sketches, the manufacturing instructions for the two components shown in Figure 7.15, as they would be interpreted by an inspection department.

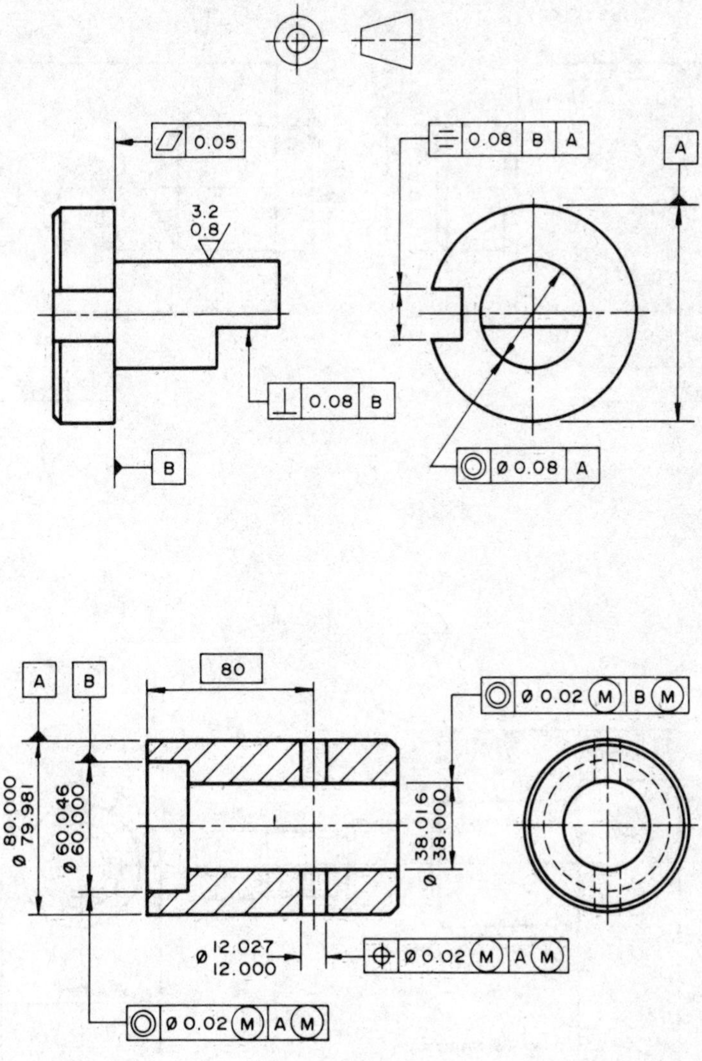

Fig. 7.15

19 Figure 7.16 shows two mating shafts with their toleranced dimensions. Using illustrative diagrams determine the largest step between surfaces X and Y under maximum material and least material conditions, and the largest possible step between the two surfaces.

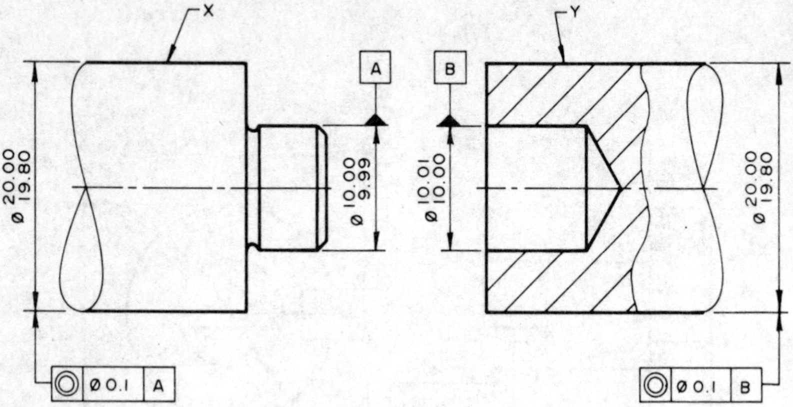

Fig. 7.16

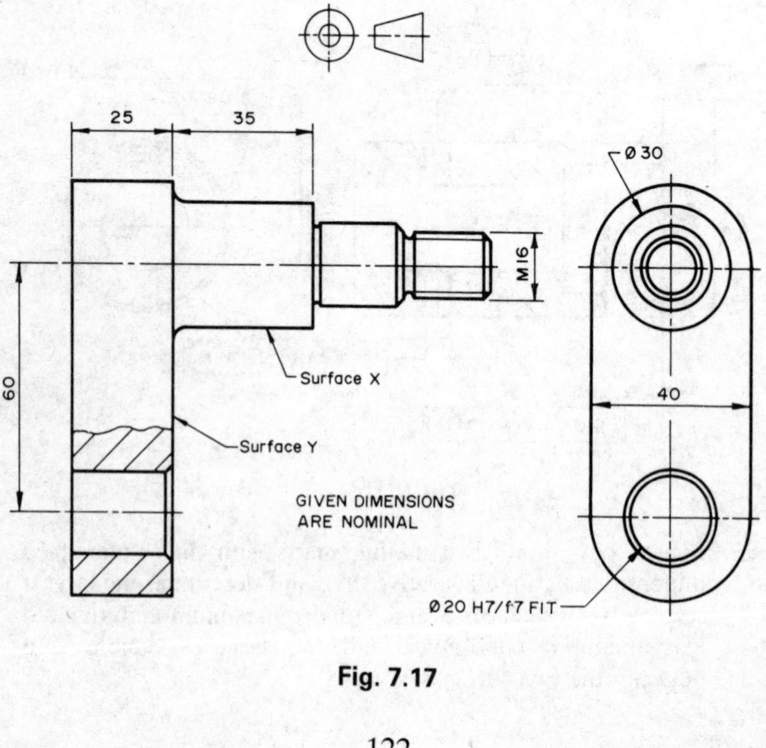

Fig. 7.17

20 Two similar components, one of which is shown in Figure 7.17, are assembled to form a link. They are secured with two M16 normal thickness nuts to BS 3692 and two bright washers, normal diameter, Form A, to BS 4320.
The links, 300 of which are required, are parts of a special chain drive. The material is surface hardened where necessary and the surfaces subjected to rubbing are X and Y.
Prepare a fully dimensioned drawing of the component with all necessary size and geometrical tolerances and surface-texture requirements.

21 Two shafts are to be connected by M16 studs to BS 4439 and normal thickness nuts to BS 3692, as shown in Figure 7.18.
(a) Calculate the maximum positional tolerance that can be applied to the axes of the studs when they are assembled in the flange, and to the axes of the clearance holes. The limits of size for the unthreaded portion of the studs are 16.00/15.82 mm diameter and the limits of size for the clearance holes are 17.77/17.50 mm diameter.
Check your answers by calculating and comparing the virtual sizes of the studs and the clearance holes.
(b) Make drawings of both shaft ends showing the positional tolerances calculated in (a), together with the necessary datums, etc. Apply the maximum material principle wherever possible. Show also the limits of size for the diameters of the locating spigot and its mating counterbore. Apply a suitable tolerance to the 12 mm spigot length and show a toleranced depth for the mating counterbore. The studs have coarse threads to tolerance class 6g.
(c) It is decided to change the design by replacing the M16 studs by M16 bolts to BS 3692, which pass through similar diameter clearance holes in both flanges and are secured by normal thickness nuts. The limits of size for the unthreaded shank of M16 bolts are 16.00/15.73 mm diameter. What will now be the maximum positional tolerance which can be applied to the axes of the clearance holes?
(d) Features whose geometrical tolerances are modified by the application of the maximum material principle may be checked for compliance with those geometrical

tolerances by fixed gauges. Such gauges simulate the mating part.

Make a sketch showing the essential features of a gauge which will check the position of the clearance holes in the flanges when they are secured by M16 bolts and nuts. Show basic dimensions only.

22 Details of a small clutch are given in Figure 7.19.

(a) Calculate the maximum values of the symmetry tolerances that can be applied to the median planes of the tongues on the sliding collar and the slots in the fixed collar.

Check your values by calculating and comparing the virtual sizes of the tongues and slots.

(b) Draw both collars showing the symmetry tolerances calculated in (a), and all necessary datums, etc. Apply the maximum material principle wherever possible. The bore of the fixed collar is made to the same tolerance as the bore of the sliding collar. Give a suitable tolerance to the 10 mm length of the tongue and show a suitable toleranced dimension for the depth of the mating slot.

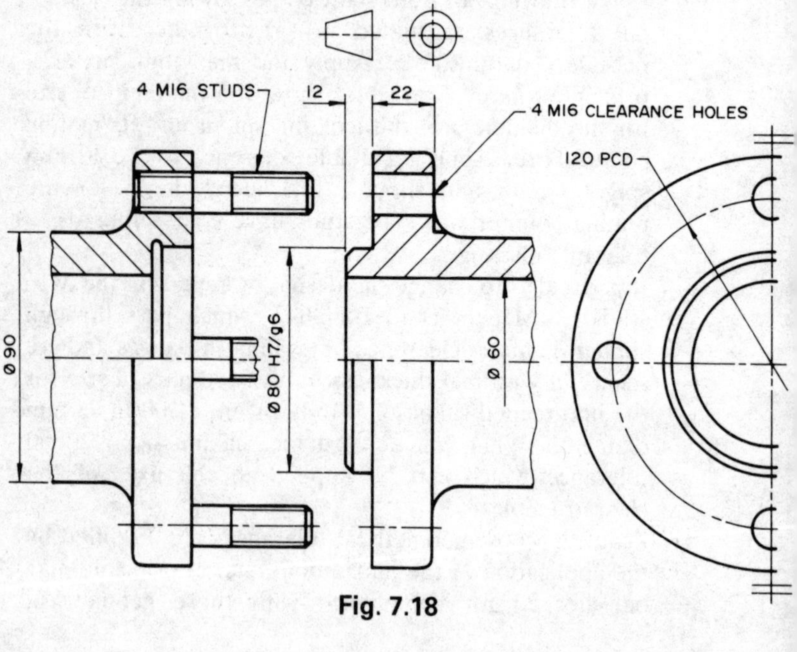

Fig. 7.18

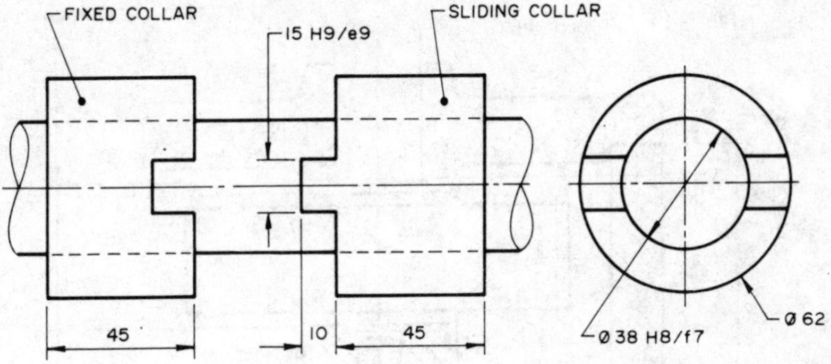

Fig. 7.19

Make any modifications to the basic design in Figure 7.19 that will assist the functioning of the clutch.

(c) Make a sketch showing a method of securing the fixed collar to the shaft.

23 Figure 7.20(a) shows part of a small gearbox with the basic sizes of the functional dimensions that control the required clearance of 0.25/0.05 mm.

(a) Calculate suitable limits of size for the functional dimensions, assuming that the 60 mm dimension on the casing is the most difficult to control and the 10 mm thickness of the spacer is the easiest.

(b) Explain how the toleranced dimension for the spacer, calculated in (a), could be changed to provide 0.1 mm tolerances on all the other functional dimensions.

(c) It is decided to modify the gearbox by adding bushes to the cover and casing, as shown in Figure 7.20(b), while maintaining the required clearance of 0.25/0.05 mm. Calculate suitable limits of size for the functional dimensions to allow for the addition of the bushes.

(d) Explain with the aid of sketches how the tolerances for the functional dimensions may be kept at the values calculated in (a) after the addition of the bushes.

24 For the piston assembly shown in Figure 7.21 the functional requirement is indicated by the 210.3/210.0 mm dimension. This is to be met when the end of the piston is against the inner surface of the cap, as shown in the figure.

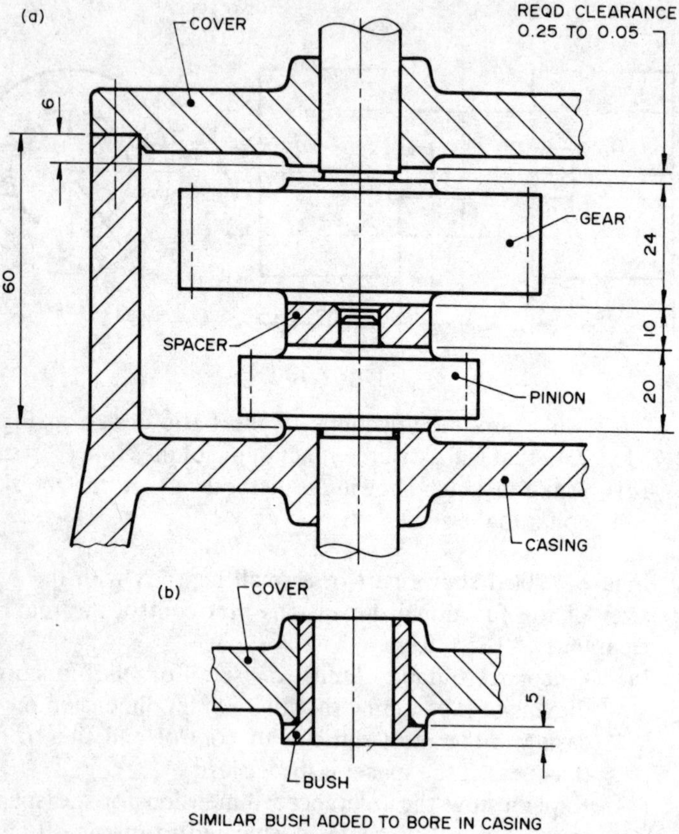

Fig. 7.20

(a) Take a Xerox print of Figure 7.21 and mark on it the functional dimensions. Scale these dimensions to find their basic sizes and apply suitable tolerances to them so that the functional requirement is met.

(b) Make sketches to show how the design of the assembly may be changed to reduce the number of functional dimensions to three and determine suitable toleranced sizes for them.

25 Computer-aided draughting and computer-aided design systems are now installed in some engineering companies.

(a) Discuss the implications of this in terms of staff, cost and efficiency.

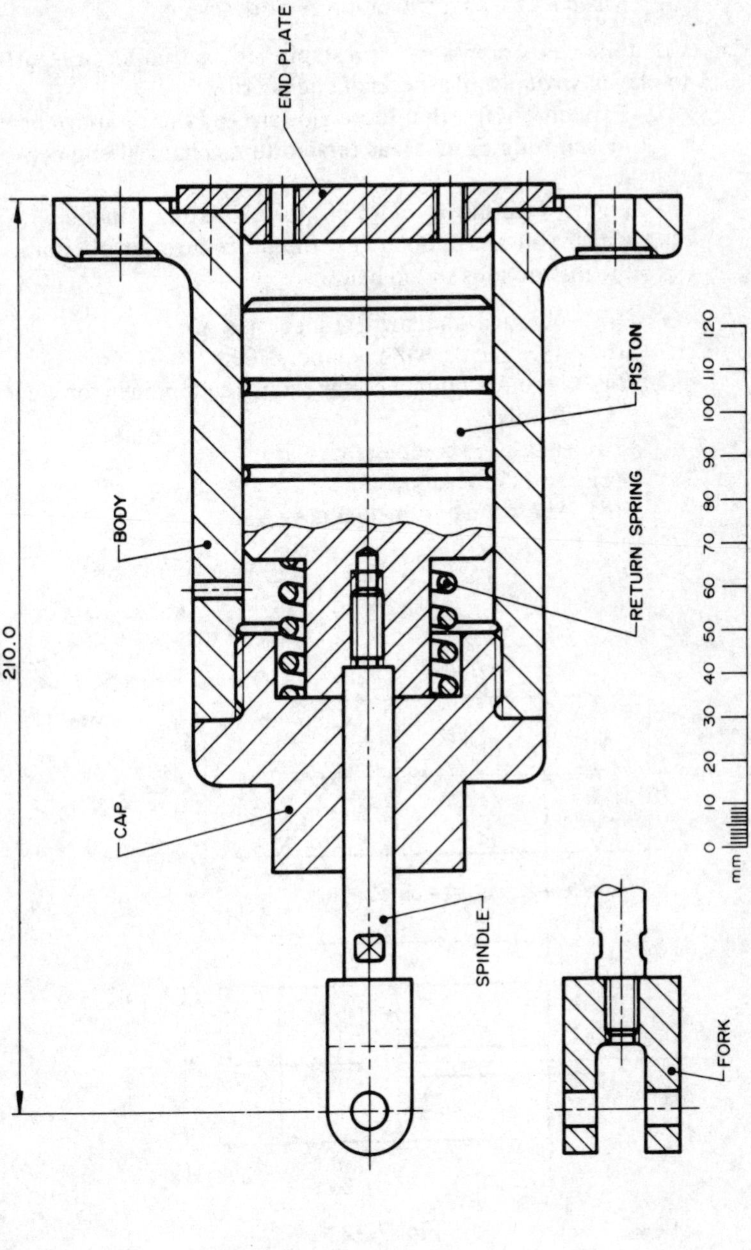
END PLATE
PISTON
BODY
RETURN SPRING
CAP
SPINDLE
FORK
210.3
210.0
0 10 20 30 40 50 60 70 80 90 100 110 120
mm

Fig. 7.21

(b) Describe with the aid of a block diagram, the equipment which forms a typical graphics work system.

26 Computer aids now have an established and important part to play in virtually all aspects of engineering.

(a) Explain briefly what these aids are and their importance by selecting three areas related to mechanical engineering.

(b) Figure 7.22 shows views of a block. Using a menu with which you are familiar, list the procedure for obtaining the instructions stated below:

1. (a) obtain a standard 2D sheet size A3;
   (b) give the drawing number 0100.
2. (a) obtain all the necessary construction lines for view B only;
   (b) line-in to complete view B;
   (c) add dimension 90;
   (d) show the cutting plane A–A.

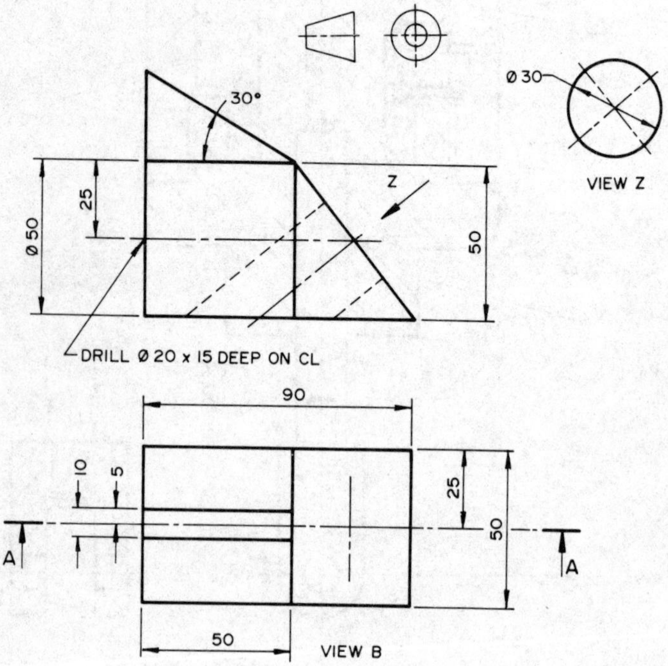

Fig. 7.22

3. (a) obtain a section through A–A;
   (b) state A–A in text and place it where appropriate;
   (c) save the sheet.

27 The development cost of a new product is estimated to be £5000 with a tooling cost of £3250. Sales of the product have been estimated at between 2500 and 3000 units in the first year. The manufacturing cost is to be £8.375 per unit.
If the selling price is £13.75 per unit, what is the break-even point? How much profit will the plant make if the selling cost is taken as 25 per cent of the manufacturing cost? If the manufacturing cost rose to £10.675 per unit, what must the new selling price be to make the same profit as originally planned?

28 Consideration is being given by the design office to the production of the cover plate and spring retainer shown in Figure 7.23, either in bakelite, as a moulding with no further machining, or in LM18 to BS 1490, as a casting followed by machining. The figure shows the bakelite product as the left-hand half and the LM18 product as the right-hand half.
In bakelite the die cost is £192 and the cost per moulding is 9.5 pence. In LM18 the pattern cost is £10, the tooling cost is £80 and the cost of casting and machining is £10 per part.
The machining is planned as follows: chuck on centre, turn and face external flange both sides and edge; locate on outer flange, turn centre; locate in fixture, drill eight holes.
How many parts in LM18 could be produced for the cost of the bakelite mould and above what production numbers will the bakelite cover plate be cheaper?

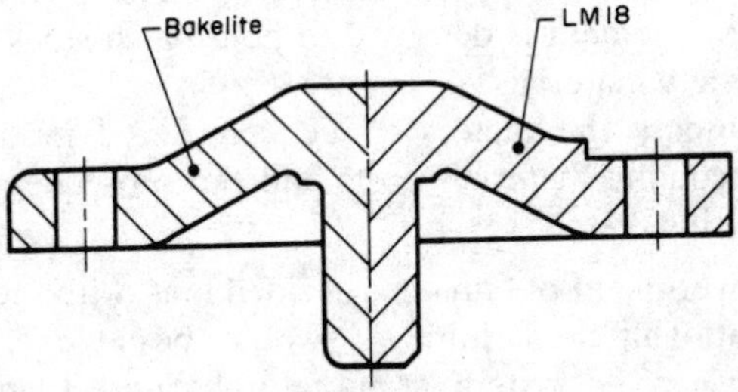

Fig. 7.23

29 A manufacturer of small electric hand tools such as drills, sanders, hedge clippers and buffers had sales of £1 000 000 last year but made a gross profit of only £100 000. The main cause of the problem appeared to be failure to increase the sales prices to meet increased labour costs of £375 000 and increased raw material costs of £400 000 during the year.

At a staff meeting the production manager suggested that an increase of 25 per cent in the selling prices of their products would place the company in a good profit position again. But the sales manager disagreed strongly, claiming that such a large price increase would drive the company out of the market. After discussion both men agreed that the net result of such a price increase would be a 10 per cent decrease in sales and production. The chief engineer proposed an alternative – plant modernization and cost reduction. By making some long-overdue improvements in the operating equipment and by buying some more efficient machines at a probable cost of £100 000 for both items, he estimated that costs could be reduced by 25 per cent.

Analyse the data for both proposals and make a report to the managing director showing which is the better and explaining why.

30 (a) Construct a 'Gozinto' or 'explosion' diagram for the initial cost estimation for production of the garden edging shears shown in Figure 7.24.

The company employs about 400 people and makes many other kinds of gardening equipment. Its workshops are not large so that the concentration of effort is on simple bench assembly, but it is equipped with automatic lathes, grinding wheels, a small crank press and hand-held squeeze riveters. The incoming stores arrangement is designed to hold batch stocks of cut-to-length materials.

(b) Discuss the factors to be considered in determining incoming materials costs and the subsequent manufacturing costs.

31 The government of Ouja has decided that, with the help of an international consortium, it would be able to dam the country's river system at a natural cataract and produce electrical power.

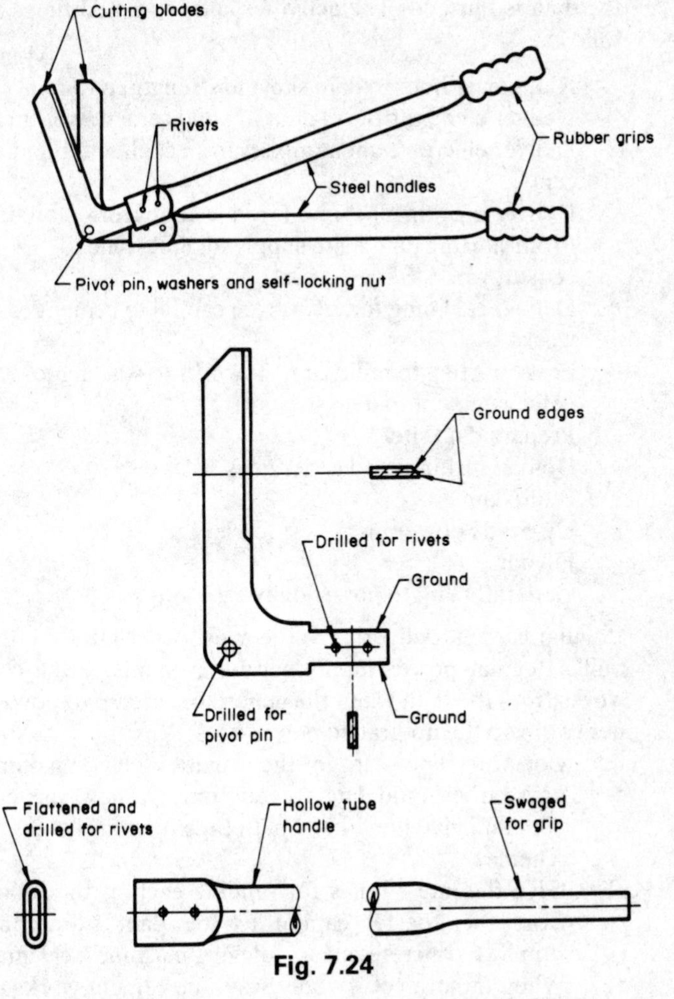

Fig. 7.24

A survey has established that near the dam site there is a large source of limestone suitable for making cement. However, the dam site is up-country and before building a cement works to supply cement to build the dam, it will be necessary to strengthen some roads, run power lines from the coastal capital and transport equipment to build the cement works. The power lines can later be up-graded to transmit power from the dam, and the cement works can provide a useful source of cement for the country's internal use, after the dam is finished. The activities and estimated times are as follows:

	Months
Run power lines to dam site and strengthen roads	5
Deliver cement from capital to build cement works	1
Deliver electric cement mixers from capital to build cement works	1
Deliver digging machines for limestone from capital	2
From starting digging to supplying limestone to cement works	2
Deliver calcining furnaces from capital to cement works	2
From starting to build cement works to starting to deliver cement to dam site	4
Prepare dam site	7
Deliver turbines and generators	2
Build dam	12
Up-grade power lines	6
Fill dam	15
Generators up to power delivery	2

Regular cement deliveries to the coast occur after the dam is built. Regular power supply will be available to the cement works from the dam when the generators are up to power and delivering to the up-graded power lines.

(a) Construct a network for the activities including dummies and earliest and latest event times. Show the critical path and give the critical path time for completion of the scheme.

(b) Give the latest times for sending each of the following from the coastal capital to the dam site: concrete supplies; concrete mixers; digging machines; calciners.

(c) When the project is under way, the cement works prove easier to build than first thought giving a saving of one month, and the installation of the calcining furnaces is phased so that a saving of two months is possible in getting the cement works operational. Consider the modified situation and show a part diagram with the new critical path and a new time to completion.

(d) The time for building the dam, although estimated, is based on much international experience and is not likely to be changed. What might be done to reduce the total time for completion?

Appendix

List of useful British Standards by chapters

Chapter	*Publication*	*Summary*
1	BS 308	Engineering drawing practice Parts 1, 2 and 3
	PP 7308	Engineering drawing practice for schools and colleges
	PD 7300	Nuts and bolts, recommended drawing ratios for schools and colleges
	BS 6381	Specification for drawing boards
	BS 3459	Specification for stands for drawing boards
2	BS 6046	Guide to the use of management, planning, review and reporting procedures Parts 1, 2, 3 and 4
	BS 4335	Glossary of terms used in project network techniques
	PD 6112	Guide to the preparation of specifications
3	PD 6481	Recommendations for the use of preferred numbers and preferred sizes
	PP 7308	Appendix B Tolerances in functional dimensioning
	BS 4500	ISO limits and fits
	BS 4500A	Data sheet: selected ISO fits – hole basis
	BS 4500B	Data sheet: selected ISO fits – shaft basis

Chapter	*Publication*	*Summary*
	PP 7309	An introduction to the tolerancing of functional length dimensions
	BS 308	Part 3 Geometrical tolerancing
	PD 7304	Introduction to geometrical tolerancing
	BS 3643	Part 2 Specification for selected limits of size, ISO threads
4	BS 1134	Method for the assessment of surface texture
	BS 2634	Specification for roughness comparison specimens
	BS 308	Part 2 Indication of surface texture and machining requirements on drawings
5	BS 6046	Part 3 Guide to the use of computers
	BS 1646	Part 4 Specification for basic symbols for process computer, interface and shared display/control functions
	BS 6650	Code of practice for control of the operation of a computer
6	BS 5750	Quality systems
	PD 6470	The management of design for economic production
	BS 6143	Guide to the determination and use of quality related costs
	PD 6495	Method for determining the advantages of (company) standardization projects